Weekly Skills Tests
Table of Contents

AUTHOR'S INTRODUCTION

Dear Educator:

Teachers have always used a variety of assessment strategies to help them evaluate student progress and to make instructional decisions. Taken together, these strategies can form a coherent assessment system.

A good assessment system has three essential elements. First, it includes a variety of informal and formal assessments. Second, it helps teachers integrate assessment during instruction and use that information to adjust their teaching. Finally, a good assessment system includes both teacher and student self-assessment throughout the learning process. *Houghton Mifflin Reading* provides teachers with assessment options to fill all these needs.

Houghton Mifflin Reading also provides extensive support for assessment integrated into the instructional plan in the *Teacher's Edition* that accompanies the anthology. There you will find informal diagnostic checks and suggestions for reteaching, student self-assessments, comprehension and fluency checks, and test-taking strategies. Other strategies are in the *Teacher's Assessment Handbook.*

Not all teachers, students, or school districts need the same assessment system. By reviewing the various options in *Houghton Mifflin Reading*, you can determine which pieces best meet your needs. Enjoy the many opportunities assessment provides to get to know your students and to help them grow.

Sheila Valencia

FEATURES AT A GLANCE

Weekly Skills Tests

✔ Are criterion referenced.

✔ Test specific skills taught each week.

✔ Include comprehension, information and study skills, structural analysis, vocabulary, spelling, grammar, and writing skills.

✔ Can be administered as individual tests before or after a skill is taught.

✔ Have a multiple-choice format with a single correct answer.

USING THE WEEKLY SKILLS TESTS

PURPOSE AND DESCRIPTION

Purpose

The Weekly Skills Tests assess students' understanding of discrete reading and language skills taught in each theme of *Houghton Mifflin Reading*. The Weekly Skills Tests are designed to help you evaluate students' understanding of these skills and use the results of the evaluation to customize future instruction to meet the needs of your class and of individual students. The tests may also be useful as preparation for certain standardized assessments.

Description

The Weekly Skills Tests are made up of tests covering comprehension, information and study skills, structural analysis, spelling, vocabulary, grammar, and writing skills. Each test includes five multiple-choice questions.

- **Comprehension Skills:** Each comprehension test includes a passage followed by multiple-choice questions that cover key concepts in the text. The test items evaluate students' ability to comprehend the reading and apply the skills to the passage.

- **Information and Study Skills:** This test is designed to assess students' ability to apply the information and study skills taught in the theme. The skills might include one of several special methods of gathering information, such as reading a map, chart, or graph, or using the dictionary.

- **Structural Analysis:** Each test is designed to assess students' ability to apply new phonics and decoding strategies. A test item might consist of a sentence to complete or one with an underlined word or phrase to explain or reword.

- **Spelling:** The spelling test assesses students' ability to recognize the correct spelling of words they have studied in a week. Students read sentences, each containing a blank. They must choose the word that is spelled correctly.

- **Vocabulary:** The vocabulary test assesses students' ability to apply new vocabulary skills. A test item might require students to identify a word that is a member of a particular word family or use a provided dictionary entry to determine the part of speech.

- **Grammar:** The grammar test checks students' understanding of the grammar skills taught in a week.

- **Writing Skills:** The writing skills test assesses students' understanding of the writing skills taught in the theme.

ADMINISTERING THE WEEKLY SKILLS TESTS

You can schedule the use of the Weekly Skills Tests in any of several ways:

- After completing a lesson, you can administer the corresponding Weekly Skills Test to help determine how well students understand the skill taught.

- You can administer selected tests at the beginning of the program or at the beginning of a theme to diagnose students' strengths and weaknesses. You can use these results to plan the appropriate level of instruction.

- You can administer any test during the course of the year in order to evaluate areas where students may need additional help.

When you administer a test, follow these guidelines:

- Check to make sure students understand how to take the test and how to mark their answers. You may wish to administer or review the Practice Test. For the Practice Test, have students read and follow the directions. Then discuss the correct answer with them. You may also want to discuss any questions students have regarding how to mark their answers.

- During the test, allow students to work independently, but help them with any directions they do not understand.

- Allow students sufficient time to complete the test.

USING TEST RESULTS TO PLAN FOR INSTRUCTION

Scoring: Using the Test Record Form

Because the Weekly Skills Tests are a simple multiple-choice evaluation, scoring is direct and objective. Correct answers are shown on the annotated pages of the *Teacher's Edition.*

In general, a score of 80 percent on any test should be accepted as an indication of satisfactory performance. Thus, if a student scores 80 percent or above, you may assume his or her understanding of a skill is adequate.

Tips for Planning Instruction

If a student demonstrates mastery of a skill application by scoring 90 percent or above, consider using the challenge suggestions throughout the *Teacher's Edition* and in the *Challenge Handbook.*

If a student answers fewer than four out of five questions correctly, he or she may need more help with the particular skill. It is important, however, to consider other evidence of a student's growth in reading (from other assessment instruments and your own observations) before concluding that the student is not performing satisfactorily. For example, you may want to review your notes on the observation checklist or the student's work on *Practice Book* pages for the skill. Monitor the student's work on similar skills in the next theme's instruction for an overall view of his or her progress. Check the Skill Finder in the *Teacher's Edition* for the next occurrence of the skill in the level. You may wish to give special attention to the student in teaching this next lesson.

If a student performs very poorly on the Weekly Skills Tests, or seems to not benefit from extra support, she or he may need intervention support. The need for intervention can be assessed using various diagnostic measures, which are outlined for you in the *Teacher's Assessment Handbook.*

For information on how to best accommodate English language learners, consult the *Language Development Resources* book.

HOUGHTON MIFFLIN READING
RESOURCES FOR REACHING ALL LEARNERS

If results from the Weekly Skills Tests determine that a student needs challenge or extra support in a certain skill area, consider modifying instruction using the following resources.

	Extra Support	Challenge
Comprehension	• *Teacher's Edition,* Throughout each selection: Extra Support/Intervention and Previewing the Text boxes; Supporting Comprehension questions; Wrapping Up questions; Review/Maintain Lessons • *Teacher's Edition,* Resources: Reteaching Lessons for Comprehension Skills • Blackline Masters: Leveled Readers; Selection Summary • Other Reading: Theme Paperbacks (below level), Classroom Bookshelf (below level)	• *Teacher's Edition,* Throughout each selection: Challenge boxes and Assignment Cards; Responding questions and activities • *Teacher's Edition,* Resources: Challenge/Extension Activities for Comprehension • Other Reading: Theme Paperbacks (above level), Classroom Bookshelf (above level)
Structural Analysis	• *Teacher's Edition,* Back to School: Phonics/Decoding Lesson in the Strategy Workshop • *Teacher's Edition,* Resources: Reteaching Lessons for Structural Analysis Skills • Intermediate Intervention • CD-ROM: Lexia Quick Phonics Assessment	• CD-ROM: Wacky Web Tales

USING THE WEEKLY SKILLS TESTS

	Extra Support	Challenge
Spelling	• Basic Words • Extra Support/Intervention box	• Challenge Words • Challenge box
Vocabulary	• *Teacher's Edition*, Extra Support/Intervention box: Vocabulary Support	• *Teacher's Edition*, Vocabulary Skills: Expanding Your Vocabulary • Resources: Challenge/Extension Activities for Vocabulary
Grammar	• *Teacher's Edition*, Resources: Reteaching Lessons for Grammar Skills	• CD-ROM: Wacky Web Tales
Writing Skills	• *Teacher's Edition*, Reading-Writing Workshop: Student Writing Sample; Tips for Getting Started; Tips for Organizing; Writing Traits; Student Self-Assessment • Writing Skills: Writing Traits	• *Teacher's Edition*, Reading-Writing Workshop: Reading as a Writer; Publishing and Evaluating • Resources: Writing Activities • Journal Writing • Revisiting the Text: Genre Lessons; Writer's Craft Lessons

If a student has overall poor test scores but does not seem to be struggling in class, check whether time allotment, directions, or test format may be contributing factors. You may review the Preparing for Testing section in the Theme Assessment Wrap-Up. Also consider the level of support a student is receiving in class. An independent task such as this test may disclose that the student is experiencing more difficulty than may have been apparent. You may want to check in the *Teacher's Assessment Handbook* for other assessment options to help you analyze the student's understanding of the tested skills.

Overall poor performance on tests and in class may indicate that the assigned work is too difficult for the student. In this instance, you may wish to have the student use the Leveled Readers during the next theme.

For more extra support and challenge ideas, consult the *Extra Support Handbook* and the *Challenge Handbook,* as well as the *Education Place* Web site.

Practice Test

Read this paragraph. Then read the question. Fill in the circle next to the best answer.

Butterflies and moths are different in several ways. Moths are active at night. Butterflies fly during the day. Butterflies have thin, smooth bodies. Most moths have thick, fuzzy bodies. There are knobs on the end of a butterfly's feelers. A moth has fuzzy feelers with no knobs. When a moth lands, it spreads its wings out flat. A butterfly holds its wings together when it is still.

1. What is this paragraph about?
- ○ **A.** how the bodies of butterflies and moths are shaped
- ○ **B.** how butterflies and moths hold their wings
- ◉ **C.** how butterflies and moths are different
- ○ **D.** how some insects fly at night and some fly in the daytime

Off to Adventure!

Level 3, Theme 1: Week 1

Weekly Skills Test Record

Student _____ Date _____

Student Record Form	Possible Score	Criterion Score	Student Score
A: Cause and Effect	5	4	
B: Base Words	5	4	
C: Spelling Short Vowels	5	4	
D: Vocabulary Dictionary: ABC Order	5	4	
E: Grammar What is a Sentence?	5	4	
F: Writing Skills Capitalizing Days and Months	5	4	
TOTAL	30	24	
Total Student Score x 3.33 =			%

Cause and Effect

Read this story. Then read each question. Fill in the circle next to the best answer.

A Hike in Bear Country

Frank's scout troop was getting set to go hiking in Montana. Frank loved camping and was excited about the trip. He went to the library and got several books about hiking in Montana. The more he read, the more worried he became. He learned that there were many bears in the mountains where they would be hiking.

On the bus ride to Montana, Frank didn't enjoy the trip because he was so worried about bears. He hardly noticed the beautiful scenery. He didn't join in the songs his friends sang and hardly ate his lunch.

The morning that the troop started up the trail, Mr. Scott, the scout master, talked to the boys about bears. "Since bears want to stay away from people, they'll leave if they hear us coming," he said. He tied some bells to each boy's walking stick. "These will give the bears plenty of warning. We'll be safe if we stay together and stay on the trail."

The bells made Frank feel a bit safer. He started enjoying the hike and being with his friends. By the end of the day, Frank was relaxed and happy. As they headed back down to camp, he thought to himself, "Bear country hiking isn't so bad!"

1. What causes Frank to begin worrying about bears?
   - ○ **A.** something that his scout master said
   - ◉ **B.** information in books that he read
   - ○ **C.** stories that his friends told about bears
   - ○ **D.** a newspaper report about a bear attack

2. Why doesn't Frank sing songs or enjoy the scenery while on the bus?
   - ○ **F.** He is carsick.
   - ○ **G.** He sleeps during the drive.
   - ○ **H.** He is angry with his friends.
   - ◉ **J.** He is worried about bears.

3. What effect do the bells have on the bears?
   - ○ **A.** They make bears too sleepy to attack.
   - ○ **B.** Bears have sensitive ears and can't stand noise.
   - ◉ **C.** They give bears warning that someone is approaching.
   - ○ **D.** Bells let bears know that people are coming so the bears can attack them.

4. What effect do the bells have on Frank?
   - ◉ **F.** He feels safe.
   - ○ **G.** He becomes nervous.
   - ○ **H.** He wakes up.
   - ○ **J.** He feels scared.

5. What happens when Frank starts enjoying the hike and his friends?
   - ○ **A.** He says that he loves hiking.
   - ○ **B.** He becomes hungry.
   - ○ **C.** He starts singing.
   - ◉ **D.** He relaxes and feels happy.

STOP

Base Words

Read each sentence. Choose the base word for the underlined word. Then fill in the circle next to the base word.

1. The family was <u>hiking</u> on the trail at sunrise.
    - ○ **A.** hiker
    - ○ **B.** hiked
    - ○ **C.** hikes
    - ◉ **D.** hike

2. They <u>prepared</u> breakfast over the campfire.
    - ○ **F.** prep
    - ○ **G.** prepar
    - ◉ **H.** prepare
    - ○ **J.** preparing

3. The son picked up leaves for his leaf <u>collection</u>.
    - ○ **A.** collecting
    - ○ **B.** collec
    - ◉ **C.** collect
    - ○ **D.** coll

4. The father and the daughter saw a beaver <u>hurrying</u> into the woods.
    - ◉ **F.** hurry
    - ○ **G.** hurries
    - ○ **H.** hurr
    - ○ **J.** hurried

5. Their <u>friendly</u> dog barked and wagged its tail.
    - ○ **A.** friends
    - ◉ **B.** friend
    - ○ **C.** frien
    - ○ **D.** friendliness

Name _____

Spelling Short Vowels

Read each sentence. Find the correctly spelled word to complete each sentence. Fill in the circle next to your answer.

1. Mei had an adventure at the history museum _____ week.
   - ○ **A.** lastt
   - ● **C.** last
   - ○ **B.** lasst
   - ○ **D.** laste

2. She was _____ behind when her class got on the bus to return to school.
   - ● **F.** left
   - ○ **H.** leeft
   - ○ **G.** lefft
   - ○ **J.** lefte

3. A guard came to _____ Mei.
   - ○ **A.** helpe
   - ○ **C.** heelp
   - ● **B.** help
   - ○ **D.** hulp

4. She and the guard looked where the buses were parked, but a _____ fog made it hard to see.
   - ○ **F.** thikk
   - ● **H.** thick
   - ○ **G.** thicke
   - ○ **J.** thik

5. Then Mei saw her teacher running _____ toward her with a big smile.
   - ● **A.** fast
   - ○ **C.** faste
   - ○ **B.** fahst
   - ○ **D.** fhast

D Name _____

Vocabulary Dictionary: ABC Order

Read each group of words. Fill in the circle next to the word that would come first in a dictionary.

1. ○ **A.** mountain
   ○ **B.** motorcycle
   ◉ **C.** month
   ○ **D.** moonlight

2. ○ **F.** hike
   ◉ **G.** high
   ○ **H.** hiss
   ○ **J.** hill

3. ○ **A.** adventure
   ○ **B.** admit
   ◉ **C.** addition
   ○ **D.** adult

4. ○ **F.** pirate
   ○ **G.** pilot
   ○ **H.** pitch
   ◉ **J.** pickle

5. ○ **A.** film
   ◉ **B.** fifty
   ○ **C.** fireplace
   ○ **D.** fist

Name _____

Grammar What Is a Sentence?

Read each question. Fill in the circle next the best answer.

1. Which of these is a sentence?
   - ○ **A.** Marty and his family.
   - ◉ **B.** They are planning a bicycle tour.
   - ○ **C.** Riding for four days.
   - ○ **D.** Camping out along the way.

2. Which of these is **not** a sentence?
   - ○ **F.** Marty has a new bike.
   - ○ **G.** His parents helped him choose it.
   - ◉ **H.** Learning the safety rules.
   - ○ **J.** He always wears a helmet.

3. Which of these is a sentence?
   - ○ **A.** Marty's sister Sandra.
   - ○ **B.** Keeping a first-aid kit.
   - ◉ **C.** The kit is in her backpack.
   - ○ **D.** Treating an injury.

4. Which of these is **not** a sentence?

○ **F.** The family drinks a lot of water.
○ **G.** Marty carries his own bottle of water.
○ **H.** He uses a special plastic glass.
◉ **J.** Folds up and fits in his pocket.

5. Which of these is a sentence?

○ **A.** The bike trails.
○ **B.** Going through woods.
○ **C.** Across fields with flowers.
◉ **D.** You don't see any cars.

Name _____

Writing Skills Capitalizing Days and Months

Read each group of sentences. Choose the sentence that shows the correct way to write days of the week and names of the months. Fill in the circle next to the best answer.

1. ○ **A.** The train museum was closed on monday and tuesday.
   ○ **B.** The train museum was closed on Monday and tuesday.
   ○ **C.** The train museum was closed on monday and Tuesday.
   ◉ **D.** The train museum was closed on Monday and Tuesday.

2. ○ **F.** The train museum is open late on Fridays and saturdays.
   ○ **G.** The train museum is open late on fridays and Saturdays.
   ◉ **H.** The train museum is open late on Fridays and Saturdays.
   ○ **J.** The train museum is open late on fridays and saturdays.

3. ○ **A.** In July and august the train museum is open seven days a week.
   ◉ **B.** In July and August the train museum is open seven days a week.
   ○ **C.** In july and august the train museum is open seven days a week.
   ○ **D.** In july and August the train museum is open seven days a week.

 Go on

4. ● **F.** On Wednesday the engineer told us that the biggest crowds ride the train on Sundays.

○ **G.** On Wednesday the engineer told us that the biggest crowds ride the train on sundays.

○ **H.** On wednesday the engineer told us that the biggest crowds ride the train on sundays.

○ **J.** On wednesday the engineer told us that the biggest crowds ride the train on Sundays.

5. ○ **A.** If your class does not go to the train museum in January, it can go in june.

○ **B.** If your class does not go to the train museum in january, it can go in june.

○ **C.** If your class does not go to the train museum in january, it can go in June.

● **D.** If your class does not go to the train museum in January, it can go in June.

Off to Adventure!

Level 3, Theme 1: Week 2

Weekly Skills Test Record

Student _____ Date _____

Student Record Form	Possible Score	Criterion Score	Student Score
A: Making Inferences	5	4	
B: Syllabication	5	4	
C: Spelling Short Vowels	5	4	
D: Vocabulary Dictionary: Multiple-Meaning Words	5	4	
E: Grammar Kinds of Sentences	5	4	
TOTAL	25	20	
Total Student Score x 4.00 =			%

Name _____

Making Inferences

Read this story. Then read each question. Fill in the circle next to the best answer.

The Surprise in the Old Barn

Ronny and his brother, Tyrone, arrived at Grandpa Jack's farm. As soon as they got there, they raced to the old barn. They couldn't wait to go exploring. At home they usually played at the park or took a bus to the mall. But they loved visiting Grandpa Jack and his farm because there were many different things to do.

"Let's see what's up in the loft," said Ronny. He climbed up the ladder, and Tyrone followed him. In the corner of the loft, they found an old trunk covered in dust.

Tyrone brushed the dust off and opened the lid. "Wow, there's a lot of old stuff in here. Look at this old rope," he said.

"And here's an old rodeo poster," said Ronny. "Hey! One of the cowboy names on it is Slim Simmons. Simmons is our last name!"

Tyrone found an old statue of a cowboy on a horse. It had the words *Grand Prize, Roping* on it. "Look at this," he said, holding it up. Tyrone thought for a moment. "Do you think that Grandpa Jack…?"

"I don't know," said Ronny before Tyrone could finish his question. "Let's go talk to Grandpa Jack right now!"

"Don't you mean Grandpa Slim?" asked Tyrone as he ran to catch up with his brother.

1. What helps you infer that the boys are excited about visiting Grandpa Jack's farm?
   - ○ **A.** They had just arrived at the farm.
   - ◉ **B.** They couldn't wait to go exploring.
   - ○ **C.** They play in the park when they are at home.
   - ○ **D.** They climb the ladder in the barn.

2. How do you think the boys feel when they find the items in the trunk?
   - ◉ **F.** They are surprised.
   - ○ **G.** They feel sad.
   - ○ **H.** They are scared.
   - ○ **J.** They feel worried.

3. What do the boys' actions tell you about them?
   - ○ **A.** They are unfair.
   - ○ **B.** They are rude.
   - ◉ **C.** They are curious.
   - ○ **D.** They are foolish.

4. Why do you think the boys' grandfather put the items in a trunk?
   - ○ **F.** He didn't have enough room in the trash.
   - ○ **G.** He moved homes and forgot to unpack them.
   - ○ **H.** There is no room in his farmhouse.
   - ◉ **J.** He wants to keep them safe.

5. What do you think the boys will ask their grandfather about?
   - ◉ **A.** what being a famous cowboy was like
   - ○ **B.** what the name of his horse was
   - ○ **C.** how the trunk got into the barn
   - ○ **D.** how he met their grandmother

STOP

Syllabication

Read each sentence. Then choose the best way to divide each underlined word into syllables. Fill in the circle next to the best answer.

1. Sandra learned to <u>snorkel</u> on her vacation.
   - ● **A.** snor • kel
   - ○ **C.** snorke • l
   - ○ **B.** sno • rkel
   - ○ **D.** sn • orkel

2. Sandra and her <u>sister</u> Jean snorkeled along the coral reef.
   - ○ **F.** siste • r
   - ○ **H.** sist • er
   - ○ **G.** si • ster
   - ● **J.** sis • ter

3. Jean pointed to a <u>stingray</u> half buried in the sand.
   - ● **A.** sting • ray
   - ○ **C.** stin • gray
   - ○ **B.** sti • ngray
   - ○ **D.** st • ingray

4. The girls saw <u>bubbles</u> coming from a scuba diver below them.
   - ○ **F.** bubb • les
   - ● **H.** bub • bles
   - ○ **G.** bu • bbles
   - ○ **J.** bubbl • es

5. Sandra saw a beautiful angelfish <u>swimming</u> near the coral.
   - ○ **A.** swi • mming
   - ○ **C.** sw • imming
   - ● **B.** swim • ming
   - ○ **D.** swimm • ing

STOP

Spelling Short Vowels

Read each sentence. Find the correctly spelled word to complete each sentence. Fill in the circle next to your answer.

1. Carla had bad _____ at the science museum yesterday.
   - ◉ **A.** luck
   - ○ **B.** luk
   - ○ **C.** lucke
   - ○ **D.** luc

2. She and the other members of the science _____ were going to the top floor to look through the telescope.
   - ○ **F.** clubb
   - ○ **G.** clube
   - ◉ **H.** club
   - ○ **J.** cluub

3. The elevator they were on got _____ between floors.
   - ○ **A.** stucke
   - ○ **B.** stuuck
   - ○ **C.** stuk
   - ◉ **D.** stuck

4. The elevator quickly became very _____.
   - ○ **F.** hoot
   - ◉ **G.** hot
   - ○ **H.** hott
   - ○ **J.** hote

5. A firefighter had to _____ a hole in the ceiling to rescue everybody.
   - ◉ **A.** chop
   - ○ **B.** chopp
   - ○ **C.** choop
   - ○ **D.** chope

Name _____

Vocabulary Dictionary: Multiple-Meaning Words

Study the dictionary entry below. Use the entry to find the answers to the questions. Fill in the circle next to the best answer.

> **litter** *noun* **1.** Paper, cans, and other trash left on the ground.
> **2.** A group of animals born to one mother at the same time.
> **3.** The board a wounded or sick person is carried on. ◆ *verb*
> **1.** To leave trash lying about: *Please don't litter the campsite.*
> **2.** To scatter around: *Clothes and toys littered his room.*
> **lit•ter** (lĭt′ ər) ◆ *noun, plural* **litters** ◆ *verb* **littered, littering**

1. Which of the following is the **second most common** definition of *litter* as a noun?
   - ○ **A.** the board a wounded or sick person is carried on
   - ○ **B.** to scatter around
   - ○ **C.** paper, cans, and other trash left on the ground
   - ◉ **D.** a group of animals born to one mother at the same time

2. Where in the entry are the other forms of the word *litter* shown?
   - ○ **F.** in the middle of the entry
   - ○ **G.** at the beginning of the entry
   - ◉ **H.** at the end of the entry
   - ○ **J.** before the entry

3. Which meaning matches the use of *litter* in this sentence?

My father didn't like it when I <u>littered</u> my room with camping gear.

- ○ **A.** to scatter around
- ○ **B.** to leave trash lying about
- ○ **C.** paper, cans, and other trash left on the ground
- ○ **D.** a group of animals born to one mother at the same time

4. Which meaning matches the use of *litter* in this sentence?

Before we left the campground, our troop picked up all of our <u>litter</u>.

- ○ **F.** to scatter around
- ○ **G.** paper, cans, and other trash left on the ground
- ○ **H.** a group of animals born to one mother at the same time
- ○ **J.** to leave trash lying about

5. Which meaning matches the use of *litter* in this sentence?

Thankfully, none of us had to be carried out of the mountains on a <u>litter</u>.

- ○ **A.** a group of animals born to one mother at the same time
- ○ **B.** to leave trash lying about
- ○ **C.** paper, cans, and other trash left on the ground
- ○ **D.** the board a wounded or sick person is carried on

Grammar Kinds of Sentences

Read each question. Fill in the circle next to the best answer.

1. Which of these is a command?
   - ○ **A.** Is that a bicycle for two?
   - ○ **B.** The back seat is small enough for a child.
   - ◉ **C.** Get on and try it.
   - ○ **D.** I've never had so much fun!

2. Which of these is a question?
   - ○ **F.** What a loud pop that was!
   - ○ **G.** Help me fix this flat tire.
   - ○ **H.** The new tube is in my backpack.
   - ◉ **J.** Do you know how to pump up the tire?

3. Which of these is an exclamation?
   - ○ **A.** We're planning a neighborhood bicycle race.
   - ◉ **B.** What a great idea that is!
   - ○ **C.** Will the race include children and adults?
   - ○ **D.** Invite your whole family to come.

4. Which of these is a statement?

   ○ **F.** What will happen after the race?

   ◉ **G.** There will be a big cookout.

   ○ **H.** It will be lots of fun!

   ○ **J.** Come and have burgers and pie with us.

5. Which of these is a command?

   ○ **A.** Can I go home right after the cookout?

   ○ **B.** First we have to pick up the trash.

   ◉ **C.** Pick up the bottles over there.

   ○ **D.** Now we can go home!

Off to Adventure!

Level 3, Theme 1: Week 3

Weekly Skills Test Record

Student _____ Date _____

Student Record Form

	Possible Score	Criterion Score	Student Score
A: Sequence of Events	5	4	
B: Information and Study Skills Parts of a Book	5	4	
C: Inflected Endings *-ed* and *-ing*	5	4	
D: Spelling Vowel-Consonant-*e*	5	4	
E: Vocabulary Dictionary: Parts of a Dictionary	5	4	
F: Grammar Subjects and Predicates	5	4	
G: Writing Skills Using Commas in Dates and Place Names	5	4	
TOTAL	35	28	
Total Student Score x 2.86 =			**%**

Sequence of Events

**Read this story. Then read each question. Fill in
the circle next to the best answer.**

Surprise Adventure

Lee's aunt was taking him on a surprise adventure. Right
after breakfast, Lee got out Aunt Terry's list that told him what
to bring. First, he found his hiking boots and then his hat.
Next, he put a hand shovel and some work gloves into his backpack. Last of all, he made a sandwich and packed a lunch.

Aunt Terry honked the horn, and Lee ran out to the car
with his pack. "Are you ready?" asked Aunt Terry.

"I think so," said Lee. "I have everything on the list."

Aunt Terry drove out into the hills. When they arrived
at the trailhead they put on their packs. "Are you ready?"
asked Aunt Terry. "We're going to hunt for fossils!"

Lee was excited! After hiking for a bit, he found a big rock
with something in it. Aunt Terry and Lee dug it out with
their shovels. After they cleaned off the rock, Aunt Terry patted
Lee on the back. "You found a shell fossil!" she said. "It was
probably formed before dinosaurs were even alive."

Lee couldn't believe it. "I've never found a fossil before," he
said. "What a great adventure! Thanks, Aunt Terry!"

1. What does Lee do before he gathers the things on the list?
   - ○ **A.** He puts on his hiking boots.
   - ◉ **B.** He eats breakfast.
   - ○ **C.** He calls his aunt.
   - ○ **D.** He packs a lunch.

2. Which of these does Lee do first?
   - ○ **F.** He makes a sandwich.
   - ○ **G.** He puts a shovel into his backpack.
   - ◉ **H.** He finds his boots and hat.
   - ○ **J.** He waits for his aunt to arrive.

3. When does Lee's aunt tell him they are going to hunt fossils?
   - ◉ **A.** after they put on their packs
   - ○ **B.** before breakfast
   - ○ **C.** after they found an interesting rock
   - ○ **D.** before Lee got into the car

4. What happens just before Lee and his aunt clean off the fossil?
   - ○ **F.** Lee thanks his aunt for taking him on the adventure.
   - ○ **G.** They drive to the trailhead.
   - ○ **H.** Lee puts on his pack.
   - ◉ **J.** They dig the rock out.

5. Which of these happened first according to the story?
   - ◉ **A.** Lee packed the things on Aunt Terry's list.
   - ○ **B.** Aunt Terry drove to the hills.
   - ○ **C.** Lee found the shell fossil.
   - ○ **D.** Lee packed his lunch.

B Name _____

Information and Study Skills
Parts of a Book

Read each question. Then fill in the circle next to the best answer.

1. On which page of a book would you find the name of its author?
    - **A.** title page
    - **B.** table of contents
    - **C.** glossary
    - **D.** index

2. In which part of a book would you find a list of words and their meanings?
    - **F.** title page
    - **G.** table of contents
    - **H.** glossary
    - **J.** index

3. Which of these chapter titles would give you information about steering a boat?
    - **A.** Chapter 1: Sailing
    - **B.** Chapter 2: Parachuting
    - **C.** Chapter 3: Rock Climbing
    - **D.** Chapter 4: Scuba Diving

4. Which part of a book lists all the subjects covered and the pages on which they are found?
    - **F.** title page
    - **G.** table of contents
    - **H.** glossary
    - **J.** index

5. Where would you look in a book to find out if there is a chapter on rock climbing?
    - **A.** title page
    - **B.** table of contents
    - **C.** glossary
    - **D.** index

STOP

Name _____

Inflected Endings *-ed* and *-ing*

Read each sentence. Choose the base word and ending for each underlined word. Fill in the circle next to the best answer.

1. Sharon was <u>preparing</u> for her trip.
- ○ **A.** pre + paring
- ● **B.** prepare + ing
- ○ **C.** prepar + ing
- ○ **D.** prep + aring

2. She would be <u>assisting</u> doctors in a tiny village.
- ○ **F.** assis + ting
- ○ **G.** assi + sting
- ● **H.** assist + ing
- ○ **J.** assisti + ng

3. Her mother <u>gathered</u> some final things for the trip.
- ○ **A.** gath + ered
- ○ **B.** gathe + red
- ○ **C.** ga + thered
- ● **D.** gather + ed

4. Her father <u>snapped</u> pictures at the airport.
- ● **F.** snap + ed
- ○ **G.** snap + ped
- ○ **H.** sna + pped
- ○ **J.** snapp + ed

5. Sharon's heart was <u>pounding</u> as she got on the plane.
- ○ **A.** poun + ding
- ○ **B.** poun + ing
- ● **C.** pound + ing
- ○ **D.** pound + ng

D Name _____

Spelling Vowel-Consonant-e

Read each sentence. Find the correctly spelled word to complete each sentence. Fill in the circle next to your answer.

1. Jacob was floating away on his inner _____ in the lake.
   ○ **A.** tobbe   ○ **C.** tub
   ◉ **B.** tube   ○ **D.** toob

2. The lifeguard saw Jacob and swam to _____ Jacob.
   ○ **F.** savv   ○ **H.** saev
   ◉ **G.** save   ○ **J.** sav

3. Jacob breathed a _____ sigh when he saw the lifeguard.
   ○ **A.** hyuge   ○ **C.** hugge
   ○ **B.** hoog   ◉ **D.** huge

4. When the lifeguard brought Jacob back to shore, Jacob's mom said she had never been so worried in her _____.
   ○ **F.** lyef   ◉ **H.** life
   ○ **G.** liff   ○ **J.** lyfe

5. That night, Jacob wrote a thank-you _____ to the lifeguard.
   ○ **A.** noht   ○ **C.** nott
   ◉ **B.** note   ○ **D.** nohte

STOP

Name _____

Vocabulary Dictionary: Parts of a Dictionary

Study the dictionary entry below. Use the entry to find the answers to the questions. Fill in the circle next to the best answer.

> **litter** *noun* **1.** Paper, cans, and other trash left on the ground.
> **2.** A group of animals born to one mother at the same time.
> **3.** The board a wounded or sick person is carried on. ◆ *verb*
> **1.** To leave trash lying about: *Please don't litter the campsite.*
> **2.** To scatter around: *Clothes and toys littered his room.*
> **lit•ter (lĭt′ ər)** ◆*noun, plural* **litters** ◆ *verb* **littered, littering**

1. What **two** parts of speech is *litter?*
- ○ **A.** noun and adjective
- ◉ **B.** noun and verb
- ○ **C.** verb and plural
- ○ **D.** verb and adverb

2. What part of the dictionary entry is (**lĭt′ ər**)?
- ○ **F.** the first meaning
- ◉ **G.** the pronunciation
- ○ **H.** the part of speech
- ○ **J.** the entry word

3. Which of the following correctly shows the syllables for *litter?*

- ○ **A.** li•tter
- ◉ **B.** lit•ter
- ○ **C.** litt•er
- ○ **D.** l•itter

4. Which of the following is a definition of *litter* as a verb?

- ○ **F.** Please don't litter the campsite.
- ○ **G.** a group of animals born to one mother at the same time
- ◉ **H.** to scatter around
- ○ **J.** the board a wounded or sick person is carried on

5. What is the plural of *litter?*

- ○ **A.** litteres
- ○ **B.** littering
- ○ **C.** littered
- ◉ **D.** litters

Name _____

Grammar Subjects and Predicates

Read each question. Fill in the circle next to the best answer.

1. What is the subject of this sentence?

All the riders put their packs in the van.

- ○ **A.** All
- ○ **B.** put their packs
- ◉ **C.** All the riders
- ○ **D.** packs in the van

2. What is the predicate of this sentence?

The group rode the first ten miles in one hour.

- ◉ **F.** rode the first ten miles in one hour
- ○ **G.** The group
- ○ **H.** the first ten miles
- ○ **J.** in one hour

3. What is the predicate of this sentence?

The first riders arrived at the campsite at four o'clock.

- ○ **A.** at the campsite at four o'clock
- ○ **B.** at the campsite
- ○ **C.** The first riders
- ◉ **D.** arrived at the campsite at four o'clock

4. What is the subject of this sentence?

Everyone enjoyed a big meal after the long ride.

- ○ **F.** after the long ride
- ◉ **G.** Everyone
- ○ **H.** enjoyed a big meal
- ○ **J.** a big meal

5. What is the predicate of this sentence?

The tired riders went to bed early

- ○ **A.** The tired riders
- ○ **B.** went to bed
- ○ **C.** early
- ◉ **D.** went to bed early

Name _____

Writing Skills Using Commas in Dates and Place Names

Read each sentence. Choose the sentence that shows the correct way to use commas. Fill in the circle next to the best answer.

1. ○ **A.** Our plane landed in Durango Colorado.
    ○ **B.** Our plane landed in, Durango Colorado.
    ◉ **C.** Our plane landed in Durango, Colorado.
    ○ **D.** Our plane landed, in Durango Colorado.

2. ○ **F.** We had tickets to ride the narrow gauge train on May 24 2004.
    ○ **G.** We had tickets to ride the narrow gauge train on, May 24 2004.
    ◉ **H.** We had tickets to ride the narrow gauge train on May 24, 2004.
    ○ **J.** We had tickets to ride the narrow gauge train on May, 24, 2004.

3. ○ **A.** The train took us to Silverton Colorado and back.
    ◉ **B.** The train took us to Silverton, Colorado, and back.
    ○ **C.** The train took us to Silverton, Colorado and back.
    ○ **D.** The train took us to, Silverton Colorado, and back.

4. ⦿ **F.** We visited the town where gold was discovered on May 6, 1859.

○ **G.** We visited the town where gold was discovered on, May 6 1859.

○ **H.** We visited the town where gold was discovered on May, 6 1859.

○ **J.** We visited the town where gold was discovered on May 6 1859.

5. ○ **A.** Our plane left the airport in Denver Colorado, the next day.

○ **B.** Our plane left the airport in Denver Colorado the next day.

○ **C.** Our plane left the airport in Denver, Colorado the next day.

⦿ **D.** Our plane left the airport in Denver, Colorado, the next day.

Celebrating Traditions

Level 3, Theme 2: Week 1

Weekly Skills Test Record

Student _____ Date _____

Student Record Form	Possible Score	Criterion Score	Student Score
A: Author's Viewpoint	5	4	
B: Compound Words	5	4	
C: Spelling Long Vowels	5	4	
D: Vocabulary Word Families	5	4	
E: Grammar Common Nouns	5	4	
TOTAL	25	20	
Total Student Score x 4.00 =			%

Name _____

Author's Viewpoint

Read this story. Then read each question. Fill in the circle next to the best answer.

Memorial Day

Memorial Day is a day for remembering. We honor the soldiers who died for our country. In my town, the day is filled with traditions. The most important thing we do is decorating graves at the local cemetery. We put flags and flowers on the soldiers' graves. Then the mayor gives a speech. He talks about what the soldiers did for the country. It makes us think about how we can help our country.

Next, there is a parade down Main Street. Soldiers march in front. Boy Scouts and Girl Scouts carry banners. Next come the people who fought in wars. Some walk, and some ride in wheelchairs. Everyone cheers for them. As the flag passes, people, including the children, put their hands on their hearts. We think about the brave soldiers who died.

Then we have a town picnic. At the picnic, we listen to an inspiring speech. It is the famous Gettysburg Address. Abraham Lincoln gave the speech to honor soldiers who died in the Civil War. After the speech, we sing our favorite songs about America.

The day helps everyone remember the past. It makes us grateful to the people who fought for our country.

Go on

1. What does the author think is the most important Memorial Day tradition?
   - ○ **A.** watching the parade
   - ○ **B.** listening to the Gettysburg Address
   - ○ **C.** going to the Memorial Day picnic
   - ◉ **D.** decorating the soldiers' graves

2. How does the author feel toward people who died for their country?
   - ○ **F.** sad
   - ○ **G.** upset
   - ◉ **H.** grateful
   - ○ **J.** disappointed

3. Why does the author leave out details about children running and playing at the picnic?
   - ◉ **A.** She wants to show that the holiday has a serious meaning.
   - ○ **B.** Children are not important.
   - ○ **C.** No children were there.
   - ○ **D.** She doesn't like children.

4. Which word describes how the author feels about the Gettysburg Address?
   - ○ **F.** entertained
   - ○ **G.** bored
   - ◉ **H.** inspired
   - ○ **J.** tired

5. Which statement best represents the author's overall message?
   - ○ **A.** We should all help keep cemeteries clean.
   - ◉ **B.** We should remember those who died for their country.
   - ○ **C.** Picnics are good because they help bring people together.
   - ○ **D.** Everyone should go to a parade.

STOP

Compound Words

Read each sentence. Find the compound word and fill in the circle next to your answer.

1. My family celebrated my birthday with all of our usual traditions.
- ○ **A.** family
- ◉ **B.** birthday
- ○ **C.** celebrated
- ○ **D.** traditions

2. In the morning, my entire family came to my bedroom with balloons and sang to me.
- ○ **F.** morning
- ○ **G.** entire
- ◉ **H.** bedroom
- ○ **J.** balloons

3. In the afternoon, we had a picnic at the park and broke a piñata.
- ◉ **A.** afternoon
- ○ **B.** picnic
- ○ **C.** broke
- ○ **D.** piñata

4. Everyone gave me presents and laughed and clapped as I opened them.
- ◉ **F.** Everyone
- ○ **G.** presents
- ○ **H.** laughed
- ○ **J.** opened

5. The party didn't end until after sunset.
- ○ **A.** party
- ○ **B.** didn't
- ○ **C.** until
- ◉ **D.** sunset

C Name _____

Spelling Long Vowels

Read each sentence. Then find the correct way to spell the missing word. Fill in the circle next to your answer.

1. My granddad showed me how to decorate wooden shapes of sea _____.
   - ○ **A.** creetures
   - ● **B.** creatures
   - ○ **C.** cretures
   - ○ **D.** critures

2. I _____ the shapes different colors.
   - ○ **F.** paynt
   - ○ **G.** pant
   - ○ **H.** paynte
   - ● **J.** paint

3. Sometimes I paint the shapes red, _____, and yellow.
   - ○ **A.** grene
   - ● **B.** green
   - ○ **C.** grean
   - ○ **D.** greene

4. I glue glitter, sequins, and _____ on them.
   - ● **F.** beads
   - ○ **G.** beeds
   - ○ **H.** bedes
   - ○ **J.** beyds

5. As I'm falling asleep, the wooden sea animals seem to _____!
   - ○ **A.** plai
   - ○ **B.** pleigh
   - ● **C.** play
   - ○ **D.** playe

D Name _____

Vocabulary Word Families

Read each question. Fill in the circle next to the best answer.

1. Which word belongs in the same word family as *unhappy?*
   - ○ **A.** happen
   - ○ **B.** helpful
   - ◉ **C.** happiness
   - ○ **D.** hoping

2. Which word belongs in the same word family as *correction?*
   - ○ **F.** corner
   - ◉ **G.** incorrect
   - ○ **H.** direction
   - ○ **J.** corral

3. Which word belongs in the same word family as *repay?*
   - ○ **A.** painting
   - ○ **B.** repeat
   - ○ **C.** repair
   - ◉ **D.** payment

4. Which word belongs in the same word family as *usual?*
   - ○ **F.** unlike
   - ◉ **G.** unusual
   - ○ **H.** common
   - ○ **J.** useful

5. Which word belongs in the same word family as *move?*
   - ○ **A.** mood
   - ◉ **B.** remove
   - ○ **C.** love
   - ○ **D.** travel

Name _____

Grammar Common Nouns

Read each question. Fill in the circle next to the best answer.

1. Which words in this sentence are common nouns?

   The best athletes in the world compete every four years.

   ○ **A.** athletes, compete, years
   ○ **B.** world, every, years
   ◉ **C.** athletes, world, years
   ○ **D.** best, compete, years

2. Which word in this sentence is a common noun?

   These special games are called the Olympics.

   ○ **F.** Olympics
   ◉ **G.** games
   ○ **H.** special
   ○ **J.** These

3. Which words in this sentence are common nouns?

   Every athlete marches into the stadium for the opening ceremony.

   ○ **A.** opening, marches, athlete
   ◉ **B.** ceremony, athlete, stadium
   ○ **C.** every, athlete, ceremony
   ○ **D.** marches, stadium, athlete

4. Which word in this sentence is a common noun?

The Olympic athletes from Greece enter first.

- ○ **F.** first
- ○ **G.** Greece
- ○ **H.** enter
- ◉ **J.** athletes

5. Which words in this sentence are common nouns?

Then a runner starts the Olympic flame with a torch.

- ○ **A.** Olympic, flame, torch
- ○ **B.** runner, starts, torch
- ○ **C.** torch, flame, starts
- ◉ **D.** runner, flame, torch

Celebrating Traditions

Level 3, Theme 2: Week 2

Weekly Skills Test Record

Student _____ Date _____

Student Record Form

	Possible Score	Criterion Score	Student Score
A: Categorize and Classify	5	4	
B: Plural Endings	5	4	
C: Spelling Long *o* Sound	5	4	
D: Vocabulary Dictionary: Guide Words	5	4	
E: Grammar Proper Nouns	5	4	
F: Writing Skills Correcting Run-On Sentences	5	4	
TOTAL	30	24	
Total Student Score x 3.33 =			%

Name _____

Categorize and Classify

Read this story. Then read each question. Fill in the circle next to the best answer.

Our New Year's Celebration

I love New Year's Eve. We have a big party at my grandparents' house in the country. My aunts and uncles drive in from all around the state. My parents leave work early so we can have enough time to get there in the snow. We usually arrive first. When we do, my brother and I go sledding and then wait by the fire for our cousins to show up.

Everyone brings something for the party. Grandma bakes bread. Uncle Jerry always cooks a ham. Aunt Sarah makes a pot of black-eyed peas. My cousin Buck has a sweet tooth, so he brings brownies for everyone.

Before supper, I have fun with my cousins. Some of the older cousins play cards. Some throw snowballs at each other. The younger children play chase or hide-and-seek. Others play football in the snow.

After we eat supper, everyone bundles up and sits on the front porch. At midnight, fireworks explode in the sky. We blow horns and bang on pans. It's fun to make so much noise!

The next day everyone packs up and goes home. We will see each other again on the Fourth of July and Thanksgiving. We always have a good time, but New Year's Eve is still my favorite family celebration.

1. Which of the following would describe all the people mentioned in the first paragraph?
   - ○ **A.** relatives
   - ○ **B.** neighbors
   - ○ **C.** people
   - ○ **D.** children

2. Which of the following foods would you classify under Dessert?
   - ○ **F.** bread
   - ○ **G.** ham
   - ○ **H.** black-eyed peas
   - ○ **J.** brownies

3. What category includes all of the things the cousins do before supper?
   - ○ **A.** Contests
   - ○ **B.** Jokes
   - ○ **C.** Games
   - ○ **D.** Sports

4. Which of these belongs in the category My Family's New Year's Eve Traditions?
   - ○ **F.** sleeping outside
   - ○ **G.** going to sleep early
   - ○ **H.** playing only indoor games
   - ○ **J.** watching fireworks

5. Which category includes Fourth of July, Thanksgiving, and New Year's Eve?
   - ○ **A.** Days of the Week
   - ○ **B.** Holidays
   - ○ **C.** Games
   - ○ **D.** Vacations

STOP

Plural Endings

Read each sentence. Choose the correct base word and ending for each underlined word. Fill in the circle next to the best answer.

1. Our neighborhood has block <u>parties</u> all summer long.
   - ○ **A.** party + s
   - ◉ **B.** party + es
   - ○ **C.** parti + es
   - ○ **D.** parti + es

2. We close off the streets and put out picnic <u>tables</u> for the food.
   - ○ **F.** table + es
   - ○ **G.** tables + s
   - ◉ **H.** table + s
   - ○ **J.** tabl + es

3. All of the <u>families</u> bring good food to share.
   - ◉ **A.** family + es
   - ○ **B.** family + s
   - ○ **C.** family + ies
   - ○ **D.** famili + es

Go on ⇨

4. Some of the neighbors like to give <u>speeches</u> about how much they enjoy the neighborhood.

○ **F.** speech + s

◉ **G.** speech + es

○ **H.** speeche + s

○ **J.** spee + ches

5. When the fun is over, we use paper <u>towels</u> to clean up.

○ **A.** tow + les

○ **B.** towel + es

○ **C.** tow + els

◉ **D.** towel + s

C

Spelling Long *o* Sound

**Read each sentence. Then find the correct way to spell
the missing word. Fill in the circle next to your answer.**

1. _____ of my family members make clay pots.
   - ○ **A.** Mowst
   - ⬤ **B.** Most
   - ○ **C.** Moast
   - ○ **D.** Moste

2. I _____ that my grandmother wants me to learn to make them.
   - ○ **F.** knoe
   - ○ **G.** kno
   - ○ **H.** knoa
   - ⬤ **J.** know

3. She tells me the _____ family would be proud of me.
   - ○ **A.** whol
   - ⬤ **B.** whole
   - ○ **C.** whool
   - ○ **D.** whoal

4. Grandmother gives me my _____ pot to decorate.
   - ⬤ **F.** own
   - ○ **G.** oan
   - ○ **H.** ohne
   - ○ **J.** owne

5. I paint a red _____ on a blue ocean on the pot.
   - ○ **A.** bowt
   - ○ **B.** bote
   - ⬤ **C.** boat
   - ○ **D.** boate

Name _____

Vocabulary Dictionary: Guide Words

Use the guide words on the dictionary page below to answer the questions. Fill in the circle next to the best answer.

> **parrot / paw**
>
> **parrot** *noun* **1.** A brightly colored tropical bird having a hooked beak: *The parrots in Mexico have lots of yellow feathers.* **2.** Someone who repeats or copies something without understanding. ◆ *verb* To repeat or copy without understanding: *I have to be careful what I do since my brother parrots my actions.*
> **par•rot (pär′ ət)** ◆ *noun, plural* **parrots** ◆ *verb* **parroted, parroting, parrots**

1. Which of the following words would appear on the page with the guide words **parrot / paw?**
   - ○ **A.** parent
   - ○ **B.** parquet
   - ◉ **C.** path
   - ○ **D.** pay

2. Which of the following words would **not** appear on the page with the guide words **parrot / paw?**
   - ○ **F.** pavement
   - ◉ **G.** parody
   - ○ **H.** patrol
   - ○ **J.** passenger

theater/thirst

theater *noun* **1.** A building where plays or movies are presented. **2.** The writing and performing of plays: *I'm writing a report on the history of the theater.*
the•a•ter (thē′ ə tər) ◆ *noun, plural* **theaters**

3. Which of the following words would appear on the page with the guide words **theater/thirst?**
   - ○ **A.** thankful
   - ◉ **C.** they
   - ○ **B.** the
   - ○ **D.** thirty

4. Which of the following words would **not** appear on the page with the guide words **theater/thirst?**
   - ○ **F.** thick
   - ○ **H.** thief
   - ○ **G.** their
   - ◉ **J.** thoughtful

boast/brain

boast *verb* **1.** To talk with too much pride: *He is always boasting about his grades.* ◆ *noun* A statement in which a person brags
boast (bōst) ◆ *verb* **boasted, boasting, boasts** ◆ *noun, plural* **boasts**

5. Which of the following words would appear on the page with the guide words **boast/brain?**
   - ○ **A.** board
   - ○ **C.** breathe
   - ○ **B.** brake
   - ◉ **D.** boil

Name _____

Grammar Proper Nouns

Read each question. Fill in the circle next to the best answer.

1. Which word in this sentence is a proper noun?

A man in France planned the first Olympic games for athletes from around the world.

- ○ **A.** man
- ◉ **B.** France
- ○ **C.** games
- ○ **D.** world

2. Which word in this sentence is a common noun?

His full name was Baron Pierre de Coubertin.

- ○ **F.** His
- ○ **G.** full
- ◉ **H.** name
- ○ **J.** Pierre de Coubertin

3. Which words in this sentence are proper nouns?

The first modern Olympic games were held in Athens, Greece, in 1896.

- ○ **A.** games, Athens
- ◉ **B.** Greece, Athens
- ○ **C.** Olympic, Greece
- ○ **D.** modern games

4. Which is one word in this sentence that is **not** a proper noun?

The first modern champion of the Olympics was James B. Connolly of the United States.

- ○ **F.** Connolly
- ○ **G.** United States
- ○ **H.** Olympics
- ◉ **J.** champion

5. Which words in this sentence are proper nouns?

The 1900 Olympic games were held in Paris, France.

- ○ **A.** Olympic, games
- ○ **B.** were, held
- ◉ **C.** Paris, France
- ○ **D.** The 1900

Writing Skills Correcting Run-On Sentences

**Read each run-on sentence. Then choose the best way
to correct the sentence. Fill in the circle next to
the best answer.**

1. My family spends every Thanksgiving at a nursing home we help
   prepare dinner and entertain the people who live there.

   ○ **A.** My family spends every Thanksgiving at a nursing home
   and we help prepare dinner. And we entertain the people
   who live there.

   ○ **B.** My family spends every Thanksgiving at a nursing home
   we help prepare dinner and so we also entertain the
   people who live there.

   ○ **C.** My family spends every Thanksgiving. It is at a nursing
   home and we help prepare dinner and entertain the
   people who live there.

   ◉ **D.** My family spends every Thanksgiving at a nursing home.
   We help prepare dinner and entertain the people who
   live there.

2. My mom is a great cook she bakes ten pies to take to the
   celebration and there are never any left.

   ◉ **F.** My mom is a great cook. She bakes ten pies to take
   to the celebration. There are never any left.

   ○ **G.** My mom is a great cook who bakes ten pies.

   ○ **H.** My mom is a great cook and she bakes ten pies to take
   to the celebration and there are never any left.

   ○ **J.** My mom is a great cook she bakes ten pies. She takes
   them to the celebration and there are never any left.

3. Dad has a secret recipe for dressing it has been in his family for years and he makes it every year.

- ○ **A.** Dad has a secret recipe for dressing it has been in his family for years. He makes it every year.
- ◉ **B.** Dad has a secret recipe for dressing. It has been in his family for years. He makes it every year.
- ○ **C.** Dad has a secret recipe for dressing. And he makes it every year.
- ○ **D.** Dad has a secret recipe for dressing and it has been in his family for years and he makes it every year.

4. I help my sister make decorations they are colorful and we put them on the walls.

- ○ **F.** I help my sister make decorations and they are colorful. We put them on the walls.
- ◉ **G.** I help my sister make decorations. They are colorful. We put them on the walls.
- ○ **H.** I help my sister make decorations on the wall and they are colorful.
- ○ **J.** I help my sister make decorations. We put them on the wall.

5. I also help set the table I put down all the plates and everybody says I do a good job.

- ○ **A.** I also help set the table. I put down all the plates and everybody says I do a good job.
- ○ **B.** I also help set the table and I put down all the plates. Everybody says I do a good job.
- ◉ **C.** I also help set the table. I put down all the plates. Everybody says I do a good job.
- ○ **D.** I also help set the table. I put down all the plates and everybody. I do a good job.

STOP

Celebrating Traditons

Level 3, Theme 2: Week 3

Weekly Skills Test Record

Student _____ Date _____

Student Record Form	Possible Score	Criterion Score	Student Score
A: Noting Details	5	4	
B: Information and Study Skills Taking Notes	5	4	
C: Contractions *'re, 's, n't, 'll*	5	4	
D: Spelling Three-Letter Clusters	5	4	
E: Spelling Unexpected Consonant Patterns	5	4	
F: Vocabulary Rhyming Words	5	4	
G: Grammar Singular and Plural Nouns	5	4	
H: Writing Skills Writing Complete Sentences	5	4	
TOTAL	40	32	
Total Student Score x 2.50 =			**%**

Name _____

Noting Details

Read this story. Then read each question. Fill in the circle next to the best answer.

Kristen Learns a Family Recipe

"Mom, it's snowing too hard to play outside," complained Kristen.

"Well, then," her mother said. "This is a great afternoon to share a family tradition. I'll teach you how to make the cookies that your great-great-grandmother used to make."

Kristen was curious. "How do you know the recipe?"

"Your great-great-grandmother shared the recipe with her daughter. That was my grandmother. And she taught my mother the recipe." Kristen's mother looked at a picture of her own mother and smiled. "I still remember the smell of those wonderful cookies baking the day that Mom taught me this recipe."

Kristen couldn't wait to make the cookies. She helped her mother make the dough. They mixed butter, sugar, eggs, milk, lemon juice, and flour. While the dough chilled, Kristen and her mother made the filling. They boiled raisins in water and added sugar and vanilla. Kristen cut out circles of dough. She put a little raisin filling in each one.

When the cookies were done baking, they were soft and lemony. Best of all, there were sweet raisins in the middle.

"What other family recipes do you know?" asked Kristen. "I want to start a family recipe book!"

1. In what season does the story probably take place?
   - ○ **A.** winter
   - ○ **B.** spring
   - ○ **C.** summer
   - ○ **D.** fall

2. What does Kristen's mother remember best about the day she learned to make the cookies?
   - ○ **F.** the sweet taste of the cookies
   - ○ **G.** the weather
   - ○ **H.** stirring the dough
   - ◉ **J.** the smell of the cookies

3. How do you know that the recipe makes Kristen's mother remember her own mother?
   - ○ **A.** She tells Kristen it is a great afternoon.
   - ○ **B.** She helps Kristen make the dough.
   - ◉ **C.** She looks at her mother's picture and smiles.
   - ○ **D.** She helps Kristen gather the ingredients.

4. Which is an ingredient that Kristen uses to make the dough?
   - ◉ **F.** lemon juice
   - ○ **G.** raisins
   - ○ **H.** filling
   - ○ **J.** vanilla

5. What detail shows you that family is important to Kristen?
   - ○ **A.** She stays inside to bake.
   - ○ **B.** She looks at her grandmother's picture.
   - ◉ **C.** She wants to make a book of family recipes.
   - ○ **D.** She helps her mother make the dough.

STOP

Name _____

Information and Study Skills
Taking Notes

Read this passage. Then read each question. Fill in the circle next to the best answer.

The Quilting Tradition

The tradition of quilting began many years ago. Cloth was expensive, so people would try and find many uses for it. For example, when clothes would wear out, people would cut them up into scraps of different shapes and sizes. These pieces would then be arranged into pretty patterns and sewn together.

It took lots of time and work to make a quilt. When one woman pieced her scraps together into a pattern, she would bring it to a quilting bee. At a quilting bee, many friends would sit around a large wooden frame and help finish the quilt. They would laugh and tell stories as they worked.

People still enjoy making quilts today. First, a design is chosen for the quilt. Next, cloth pieces are cut and sewn together. This forms the quilt top. When the top is ready, a piece of cloth that is the same size as the top is laid out. This is the backing for the quilt. A sheet of stuffing, or batting, is spread on top of this. Next, with the finished side facing up, the quilt top is placed on the batting. The three layers are then stretched out smoothly on a frame. Finally, the layers are stitched together to form the finished quilt.

1. If you were taking notes, what would be the best main heading for the topic of the passage?
   - ○ **A.** Quilts of Today
   - ◉ **B.** Putting a Quilt Together
   - ○ **C.** Uses for Cloth
   - ○ **D.** Kinds of Quilts

2. Which of these details about the topic is most important?
   - ○ **F.** Quilts are made out of cloth.
   - ○ **G.** People enjoy making quilts.
   - ○ **H.** Batting is the stuffing inside a quilt.
   - ◉ **J.** Quilting is an old tradition that is still enjoyed today.

3. Which of these details about the topic is least important?
   - ○ **A.** Today, the first thing quilters do is choose a design.
   - ○ **B.** The cloth pieces are arranged into a pretty pattern.
   - ◉ **C.** Clothes wear out.
   - ○ **D.** Cloth was expensive so it was reused to make quilts.

4. What key word or words could you use that best fit the information in the second paragraph?
   - ◉ **F.** Quilting Bees
   - ○ **G.** Patterns
   - ○ **H.** Cloth
   - ○ **J.** Design

5. Which question could you ask that best fits the information in the last paragraph?
   - ○ **A.** Why are quilts still made today?
   - ◉ **B.** How is a quilt put together these days?
   - ○ **C.** What is a quilting bee?
   - ○ **D.** What is batting?

STOP

Contractions *'re, 's, n't, 'll*

Read each sentence. Choose the word or words that stand for the underlined word. Fill in the circle next to the best answer.

1. <u>We're</u> planning a Fourth of July parade for our neighborhood.
   - ○ **A.** We was
   - ○ **B.** Were
   - ◉ **C.** We are
   - ○ **D.** We would

2. Steve says <u>he's</u> planning to paint his bike red, white, and blue.
   - ○ **F.** he did
   - ○ **G.** he would
   - ○ **H.** he will
   - ◉ **J.** he is

3. Lily will be on vacation so she <u>won't</u> be able to come.
   - ○ **A.** won not
   - ◉ **B.** will not
   - ○ **C.** were not
   - ○ **D.** was not

4. Pat and Sonya say that <u>they'll</u> pass out flags to everyone who comes.
   - ○ **F.** there will
   - ○ **G.** they would
   - ◉ **H.** they will
   - ○ **J.** they were

5. Some people say <u>they're</u> going to walk their pets in the parade.
   - ◉ **A.** they are
   - ○ **B.** their
   - ○ **C.** there
   - ○ **D.** they will

STOP

Name _____

Spelling Three-Letter Clusters

Read each sentence. Then find the correct way to spell the missing word. Fill in the circle next to your answer.

1. My grandmother _____ clay onto a pottery wheel.
   - ○ **A.** thros
   - ● **B.** throws
   - ○ **C.** throes
   - ○ **D.** throwes

2. She shapes _____ large pots out of the clay.
   - ● **F.** three
   - ○ **G.** thre
   - ○ **H.** thrie
   - ○ **J.** theree

3. She uses her _____ arms to put the pots in a special oven.
   - ○ **A.** stroong
   - ○ **B.** stronge
   - ● **C.** strong
   - ○ **D.** strowng

4. The next day, we put soil in the pots and _____ on flower seeds.
   - ○ **F.** sprinkel
   - ● **G.** sprinkle
   - ○ **H.** springkle
   - ○ **J.** sprenkle

5. I _____ the seeds with water.
   - ○ **A.** spra
   - ○ **B.** spraye
   - ○ **C.** sprai
   - ● **D.** spray

Spelling Unexpected Consonant Patterns

Read each sentence. Then find the correct way to spell the missing word. Fill in the circle next to your answer.

1. I eagerly _____ my sister Emma open her kit.
    - ⬤ **A.** watch
    - ○ **B.** wawtch
    - ○ **C.** watche
    - ○ **D.** whatch

2. She takes out her needles and fanciest wool to _____.
    - ○ **F.** knite
    - ○ **G.** knet
    - ⬤ **H.** knit
    - ○ **J.** knid

3. Emma is making a blue pom pom hat to _____ Mom's blue coat.
    - ○ **A.** matche
    - ○ **B.** maytch
    - ○ **C.** mahtch
    - ⬤ **D.** match

4. When Emma is finished, I _____ the hat in pretty paper.
    - ○ **F.** wrapp
    - ○ **G.** wrape
    - ⬤ **H.** wrap
    - ○ **J.** wrhap

5. We _____ our names on a special birthday card that I made.
    - ○ **A.** wright
    - ⬤ **B.** write
    - ○ **C.** wryte
    - ○ **D.** wriite

STOP

Name _____

Vocabulary Rhyming Words

Read each question. Fill in the circle next to the best answer.

1. Which word rhymes with *write?*
- ○ **A.** ride
- ○ **B.** time
- ○ **C.** fine
- ◉ **D.** bright

2. Which word rhymes with *mountain?*
- ◉ **F.** fountain
- ○ **G.** scouting
- ○ **H.** maintain
- ○ **J.** mowing

3. Which word rhymes with *shake?*
- ○ **A.** pale
- ○ **B.** snack
- ○ **C.** shock
- ◉ **D.** break

4. Which word rhymes with *better?*

- ○ **F.** between
- ○ **G.** best
- ◉ **H.** letter
- ○ **J.** treasure

5. Which word rhymes with *spray?*

- ○ **A.** strain
- ○ **B.** sport
- ◉ **C.** weigh
- ○ **D.** price

STOP

G Name _____

Grammar Singular and Plural Nouns

Read each question. Fill in the circle next to the best answer.

1. Which word in this sentence is a plural noun?

    The ruins of an ancient Greek stadium gave Pierre de Coubertin the idea for the Olympics.

    ○ **A.** ruins
    ○ **B.** Greek
    ○ **C.** stadium
    ○ **D.** contest

2. Which word in this sentence is a singular noun?

    Judges awarded medals to the winners of each contest.

    ○ **F.** Judges
    ○ **G.** medals
    ○ **H.** winners
    ○ **J.** contest

3. Which word in this sentence is a plural noun?

    An athlete trains for years to win a medal.

    ○ **A.** athlete
    ○ **B.** years
    ○ **C.** win
    ○ **D.** trains

Go on

4. Which word in this sentence is a singular noun?

Hockey was first played in the 1920 games.

- ○ **F.** games
- ○ **G.** played
- ○ **H.** first
- ◐ **J.** Hockey

5. Which word in this sentence is a plural noun?

The first U.S. female Olympic star, Babe Didrikson, entered three track and field events.

- ◐ **A.** events
- ○ **B.** star
- ○ **C.** three
- ○ **D.** Didrikson

Name _____

Writing Skills Writing Complete Sentences

Fill in the circle next to the complete sentence.

1. ○ **A.** People in the nursing home.
    ○ **B.** Even before the Thanksgiving meal starts.
    ○ **C.** Happy to see us again.
    ● **D.** Smiling faces greet us at the door.

2. ○ **F.** Everyone in the family.
    ○ **G.** A special job to do.
    ● **H.** We take care of everything.
    ○ **J.** Such as setting the table, filling the glasses, and
       serving the food.

3. ● **A.** Everyone relaxes after a great meal.
    ○ **B.** After enjoying a great meal.
    ○ **C.** A delicious, homemade meal.
    ○ **D.** To enjoy the meal and relax afterwards.

4. ○ **F.** Putting things back in boxes.
    ○ **G.** Wash all the dishes and glasses.
    ◉ **H.** My job is to clear the table.
    ○ **J.** Any extra food in the refrigerator.

5. ◉ **A.** At last we say goodnight.
    ○ **B.** The long day over.
    ○ **C.** Hugging each other good-bye.
    ○ **D.** Very tired but happy.

STOP

Celebrating Traditons

Level 3, Theme 2: Week 4

Weekly Skills Test Record

Student _____ Date _____

Student Record Form

	Possible Score	Criterion Score	Student Score
A: Topic, Main Idea, and Supporting Details	5	4	
B: Plurals with Words Ending in *ch, sh, x, s*	5	4	
C: Spelling Long *i* Sound	5	4	
D: Vocabulary Dictionary: Definitions	5	4	
E: Grammar Special Plural Nouns	5	4	
TOTAL	25	20	
Total Student Score x 4.00 =			%

Name _____

Topic, Main Idea, and Supporting Details

Read this passage. Then read each question. Fill in the circle next to the best answer.

Fun in the Sun

Every summer, my family packs up and heads for Sunnyside Beach. The fun begins as soon as we are on the road. During the trip, we talk and sing songs. We stop for a picnic at our favorite roadside park. As we get closer to the beach, we point out familiar sights.

We always stay in the same beach house. It has big, sunny rooms and a porch with a swing. My dad loves to read in the hammock out back. The owner, Mrs. Pitts, always leaves a plate of homemade cookies on the kitchen table.

Of course, the best part of our vacation is swimming in the ocean and playing on the beach. Every morning, we go for a long swim. We draw pictures in the wet sand and make sand sculptures. In the afternoons, we take walks along the beach. We collect shells and smooth rocks.

When our vacation is over, we pack up the pretty things we've found. It's hard to leave, but we know we'll be back again next summer.

Go on

1. What is the topic of this passage?
   - **A.** a summertime tradition
   - **B.** ways to have fun with your family
   - **C.** things to do while driving with your family
   - **D.** learning to love nature

2. What is the main idea of the first paragraph?
   - **F.** The family drives to the same beach every summer.
   - **G.** They like the beach house where they always stay.
   - **H.** They stop for a picnic.
   - **J.** The drive to the beach is fun.

3. Which detail best supports the main idea of the first paragraph?
   - **A.** The owner bakes cookies for the family.
   - **B.** They talk and sing as they drive.
   - **C.** The name of the beach is Sunnyside Beach.
   - **D.** They pack the car.

4. What is the main idea of the third paragraph?
   - **F.** Playing on the beach and swimming in the ocean are fun.
   - **G.** There are shells on the beach.
   - **H.** Walking is good for you.
   - **J.** Morning is the best time for a long swim.

5. Which detail supports the main idea of the third paragraph?
   - **A.** The family always stays at the same house.
   - **B.** The family eats at their favorite roadside park.
   - **C.** The family draws pictures in the sand.
   - **D.** The father reads in the hammock.

Plurals with Words Ending in *ch, sh, x, s*

Read each sentence. Then choose the correct plural form of the word in ( ) to complete each sentence. Fill in the circle next to your answer.

1. The third-grade _____ are putting on a Thanksgiving program. (class)
   - ○ **A.** clases
   - ○ **B.** classies
   - ◉ **C.** classes
   - ○ **D.** classess

2. Mrs. Downing brought in four large _____ of costumes. (box)
   - ◉ **F.** boxes
   - ○ **G.** boxs
   - ○ **H.** boxxes
   - ○ **J.** boxies

3. The girls will be wearing old-fashioned Pilgrim _____. (dress)
   - ○ **A.** dreses
   - ◉ **B.** dresses
   - ○ **C.** dressses
   - ○ **D.** dress

4. We put picnic tables and _____ on the stage. (bench)
   - ○ **F.** benchs
   - ○ **G.** benchhes
   - ◉ **H.** benches
   - ○ **J.** benchies

5. Mr. Lyons even brought some old wooden _____ to use for the feast. (dish)
   - ○ **A.** dishhes
   - ○ **B.** dishies
   - ○ **C.** dishs
   - ◉ **D.** dishes

STOP

Name _____

Spelling Long *i* Sound

Read each sentence. Then find the correct way to spell the missing word. Fill in the circle next to your answer.

1. I decide that I _____ like to decorate a pot the way my aunt does.
   - ○ **A.** migt
   - ◉ **B.** might
   - ○ **C.** miet
   - ○ **D.** mihte

2. I _____ a pot that I think my mother would like.
   - ○ **F.** finde
   - ◉ **G.** find
   - ○ **H.** fynd
   - ○ **J.** fiend

3. I try to make the pattern that I imagine in my _____.
   - ○ **A.** miend
   - ○ **B.** mighnd
   - ◉ **C.** mind
   - ○ **D.** minde

4. I use _____ yellow and purple paints.
   - ○ **F.** brihte
   - ○ **G.** brigt
   - ○ **H.** briet
   - ◉ **J.** bright

5. When the paint _____, I give the pot to my mother as a gift.
   - ◉ **A.** dries
   - ○ **B.** dryes
   - ○ **C.** drighs
   - ○ **D.** drise

D Name _____

Vocabulary Dictionary: Definitions

Study the entry on the dictionary page below. Use the dictionary page to answer the questions. Fill in the circle next to the best answer.

---

parrot / paw

parrot *noun* **1.** A brightly colored tropical bird having a hooked beak: *The parrots in Mexico have lots of yellow feathers.* **2.** Someone who repeats or copies something without understanding. ◆ *verb* To repeat or copy without understanding: *I have to be careful what I do since my brother parrots my actions.*
par•rot (pär′ ət) ◆ *noun, plural* **parrots** ◆ *verb* **parroted, parroting, parrots**

---

1. How many meanings does *parrot* have when used as a verb?
   - ○ **A.** four
   - ○ **B.** three
   - ○ **C.** two
   - ○ **D.** one

2. What is the most common definition of *parrot* as a noun?
   - ○ **F.** someone who repeats or copies something without understanding
   - ○ **G.** a brightly colored tropical bird having a hooked beak
   - ○ **H.** an animal many people keep as a pet
   - ○ **J.** to repeat or copy without understanding

3. Which definition of *parrot* applies to this sentence?

"Will you please stop <u>parroting</u> everything I say?"

- ○ **A.** someone who repeats or copies something without understanding
- ◉ **B.** to repeat or copy without understanding
- ○ **C.** a brightly colored tropical bird having a hooked beak
- ○ **D.** a pet animal

4. What is an example of *parrot* used as a noun in a sentence?

- ○ **F.** someone who repeats or copies something without understanding
- ○ **G.** a brightly colored tropical bird having a hooked beak
- ○ **H.** I have to be careful what I do since my brother parrots my actions.
- ◉ **J.** The parrots in Mexico have lots of yellow feathers.

5. Which definition of *parrot* applies to this sentence?

She's just a <u>parrot</u> who says whatever her friend says.

- ○ **A.** a brightly colored tropical bird having a hooked beak
- ○ **B.** to repeat or copy without understanding
- ◉ **C.** someone who repeats or copies something without understanding
- ○ **D.** I have to be careful what I do since my brother parrots my actions.

Name _____

Grammar Special Plural Nouns

Choose the correct plural form for the underlined noun in each sentence. Fill in the circle next to the answer you choose.

1. Our <u>country</u> has taken part in the Olympic games since 1896.
   - ○ **A.** countryes
   - ◉ **C.** countries
   - ○ **B.** country's
   - ○ **D.** countrys

2. A Russian <u>woman</u> holds the record for the most medals won by one person.
   - ○ **F.** women
   - ◉ **H.** woman's
   - ○ **G.** womans
   - ○ **J.** womens

3. Wilma Rudolph was very sick as a <u>child</u>, but she became a successful Olympic athlete.
   - ○ **A.** childes
   - ◉ **C.** children
   - ○ **B.** childrens
   - ○ **D.** childs

4. Each <u>man</u> on the 1992 "Dream Team" was a basketball star.
   - ○ **F.** mans
   - ○ **H.** man's
   - ◉ **J.** men
   - ○ **G.** mene

5. When the Greek runner Spyros Louis entered the stadium first, the crowd sent a roar into the <u>sky</u>.
   - ○ **A.** skeyes
   - ○ **C.** skis
   - ◉ **B.** skies
   - ○ **D.** skys

Incredible Stories

Level 3, Theme 3: Week 1
Weekly Skills Test Record

Student _____ Date _____

Student Record Form

	Possible Score	Criterion Score	Student Score
A: Fantasy and Realism	5	4	
B: Plurals with Words Ending in *f* and *fe*	5	4	
C: Spelling Vowel Sounds in *clown* and *lawn*	5	4	
D: Vocabulary Using Context	5	4	
E: Grammar Possessive Nouns	5	4	
TOTAL	25	20	
Total Student Score x 4.00 =			%

Name _____

Fantasy and Realism

Read this story. Then read each question. Fill in the circle next to the best answer.

A Plane Recess

It was sharing time in Mrs. Soto's kindergarten class. Troy was showing a model airplane he had made. As Troy explained how he made the plane, Angie slowly raised her hand. "Why can't we fly like airplanes?" she asked.

"We can't fly because we don't have wings," answered Troy.

"I wish I had wings," Angie said softly to herself. Just as she spoke, a stretching sound followed by a pop was heard coming from her back. Everyone gasped! Blue wings were growing out of Angie's back! At that same moment, Troy's model plane took off from his hand and flew outside to the playground where, in a puff of smoke, it blew up into a full-sized jumbo jet!

Angie took off from her desk and flew over the crowd that was now gathered around the noisy jet. She circled twice above the plane and the crowd before landing on the plane's wing and climbing through one of its windows. Once Angie was inside, the plane began to rumble and shake and make even more noise. It started to roll forward across the kickball field. Soon, the plane had enough speed and it lifted off the ground. Troy waved at Angie, who was sitting in the pilot's chair.

Mrs. Soto was shocked and unsure of what she should do. She finally realized what time it was. "Class," she said with a big smile, "I believe it's time for recess."

1. What is the **first** clue that this story is a fantasy?
   - ○ **A.** The class has sharing time.
   - ○ **B.** Angie raises her hand to ask a question.
   - ○ **C.** Angie wishes she had wings.
   - ◉ **D.** Angie grows wings.

2. Which of these objects could **not** be found at a real school?
   - ○ **F.** a model airplane
   - ◉ **G.** a jumbo jet
   - ○ **H.** desks
   - ○ **J.** a kickball field

3. Which of these could really happen?
   - ◉ **A.** A boy makes a model plane.
   - ○ **B.** A person grows wings.
   - ○ **C.** A model plane changes into a jumbo jet.
   - ○ **D.** A kindergartner flies a jumbo jet.

4. Which of these could **not** happen at a school?
   - ○ **F.** The teacher says it is time for recess.
   - ○ **G.** Students have sharing time in the classroom.
   - ◉ **H.** A jumbo jet takes off from the playground.
   - ○ **J.** A crowd of people gather on the playground.

5. Which of these could really happen?
   - ○ **A.** Troy's model plane takes off from his hand.
   - ○ **B.** Angie lands on the plane's wing.
   - ○ **C.** Angie flies over the crowd.
   - ◉ **D.** Mrs. Soto is shocked.

Plurals with Words Endings in *f* and *fe*

Read each sentence. Choose the correct base word for each underlined word. Fill in the circle next to your answer.

1. The men waved goodbye to their <u>wives</u> and left on their walk.
   - ● **A.** wife
   - ○ **B.** wive
   - ○ **C.** wiv
   - ○ **D.** wif

2. The men were carrying <u>loaves</u> of bread and some cheese.
   - ○ **F.** loafe
   - ● **G.** loaf
   - ○ **H.** loav
   - ○ **J.** loave

3. They came across tracks of <u>wolves</u> along the path.
   - ○ **A.** wolv
   - ○ **B.** wolfe
   - ○ **C.** wolve
   - ● **D.** wolf

4. The animals were lying in a pile of fallen <u>leaves</u>.
   - ○ **F.** leafe
   - ○ **G.** leav
   - ● **H.** leaf
   - ○ **J.** leafs

5. "Don't you wonder what their <u>lives</u> are like?" one of the animals said.
   - ○ **A.** live
   - ○ **B.** liv
   - ○ **C.** lif
   - ● **D.** life

STOP

Spelling Vowel Sounds in *clown* and *lawn*

Read each sentence. Then find the correct way to spell the missing word. Fill in the circle next to your answer.

1. Jackie was _____ on her cell phone in the back yard.
   ○ **A.** tawking   ◉ **C.** talking
   ○ **B.** tauking   ○ **D.** taulking

2. She heard a loud rumbling _____.
   ○ **F.** sownd   ◉ **H.** sound
   ○ **G.** sawnd   ○ **J.** saund

3. She looked _____.
   ○ **A.** downe   ◉ **C.** down
   ○ **B.** daun   ○ **D.** doune

4. Suddenly, the whole _____ swelled up into a big, grassy lump.
   ○ **F.** laun   ○ **H.** lon
   ◉ **G.** lawn   ○ **J.** lahn

5. Jackie watched as a giant flower grew out of the _____.
   ◉ **A.** ground   ○ **C.** grown
   ○ **B.** groun   ○ **D.** grownd

Vocabulary Using Context

Read each sentence. Choose the correct meaning for each underlined word. Fill in the circle next to your answer.

1. Hannah tried to <u>assail</u> the killer bee with a stick but struck her younger brother Mike in the nose instead.
   - ○ **A.** catch
   - ○ **B.** glide
   - ◉ **C.** attack
   - ○ **D.** float

2. Mike's face had a look of <u>agony</u>.
   - ○ **F.** happiness
   - ◉ **G.** great pain
   - ○ **H.** disorder
   - ○ **J.** glitter

3. There was a <u>considerable</u> bump on his nose.
   - ○ **A.** caring
   - ◉ **B.** large
   - ○ **C.** kind
   - ○ **D.** tiny

Go on ⇨

4. Hannah said she was sorry and covered Mike's nose with <u>gauze</u>.

○ **F.** a blanket
○ **G.** a sticker
◉ **H.** a bandage
○ **J.** a hat

5. To <u>atone</u> for hurting Mike, Hannah took him out for ice cream.

○ **A.** forget
○ **B.** remind
○ **C.** travel
◉ **D.** make up

Name _____

Grammar Possessive Nouns

Read each sentence. Choose the correct possessive to replace the underlined words. Fill in the circle next to the best answer.

1. The twins always enjoyed visiting <u>the garden of their uncle</u>.
   - ○ **A.** their uncles' garden
   - ● **B.** their uncle's garden
   - ○ **C.** their uncles garden
   - ○ **D.** their uncle garden's

2. <u>The favorite place for the twins</u> was the lily pond.
   - ● **F.** The twins' favorite place
   - ○ **G.** The twin's favorite place
   - ○ **H.** The twins favorite place
   - ○ **J.** The twins favorite place's

3. They delighted in <u>the flowers of each water lily</u>.
   - ○ **A.** each water lilys flowers
   - ○ **B.** each water lily flowers
   - ● **C.** each water lily's flowers
   - ○ **D.** each water lilys' flowers'

4. They liked listening to <u>the croaks of the frogs</u>.
   - ○ **F.** the frog's croaks
   - ○ **G.** the frogs croaks
   - ○ **H.** the frog croaks'
   - ● **J.** the frogs' croaks

5. <u>The calm of the lily pond</u> was what the twins enjoyed most.
   - ○ **A.** The lily's pond calm
   - ○ **B.** The lily ponds calm
   - ● **C.** The lily pond's calm
   - ○ **D.** The lily pond's calms

Incredible Stories

Level 3, Theme 3: Week 2

Weekly Skills Test Record

Student _____ Date _____

Student Record Form	Possible Score	Criterion Score	Student Score
A: Following Directions	5	4	
B: Information and Study Skills Using an Atlas	5	4	
C: Word Endings -er and -est	5	4	
D: Spelling Vowel + /r/ Sounds	5	4	
E: Vocabulary Dictionary: Choosing the Correct Meaning	5	4	
F: Grammar What Is a Verb?	5	4	
G: Writing Skills Using Commas for Direct Address	5	4	
TOTAL	35	28	
Total Student Score x 2.86 =			%

Name _____

Following Directions

**Read this story. Then read each question. Fill in
the circle next to the best answer.**

Giant Stew

Carl had a problem. His giant, Pete, was always hungry. No
matter what Carl brought him to eat, Pete always gulped it down
in one bite.

One day, Carl heard the giant sigh and say, "Oh, if only I
could have one steaming bowl of Giant Stew!" Carl looked in
every cookbook he had. Finally he found this recipe.

Giant Stew

1 gallon of olive oil	80 pounds of potatoes
50 onions	40 gallons of tasty broth
25 cloves of garlic	plenty of salt
100 carrots	lots of pepper

First, mash the garlic and chop up the onions, carrots, and potatoes. Second, heat the oil in a very large
tub. Then cook the onions and garlic for 8 minutes.
Next, add the carrots, potatoes, and broth. Bring to a
boil. Add several big handfuls of salt and pepper.
Finally, turn down the heat and cook the stew on low
for 8 hours. Serve and make your giant very happy.

Carl followed the directions carefully. When the stew was
ready, he called Pete to dinner. When Pete saw the huge tub of
giant stew, he was very happy. He lifted Carl up and held him
against his giant cheek. "You are the best friend a giant could
have," he said.

Go on ⟹

---

1. How many ingredients does Carl need for making the stew?
   - ○ **A.** four
   - ◉ **B.** eight
   - ○ **C.** nine
   - ○ **D.** seven

2. What is the third step in making the stew?
   - ○ **F.** Boil the broth.
   - ○ **G.** Mash the garlic.
   - ○ **H.** Add salt.
   - ◉ **J.** Cook onions and garlic.

3. What does Carl do before he heats the oil?
   - ◉ **A.** He chops up potatoes.
   - ○ **B.** He mixes the carrots, potatoes, and broth.
   - ○ **C.** He cooks the stew for eight hours.
   - ○ **D.** He adds pepper.

4. When does Carl add the salt and pepper?
   - ○ **F.** before he heats the oil
   - ◉ **G.** after the mixture starts to boil
   - ○ **H.** before he adds the broth
   - ○ **J.** after he serves the stew

5. What would probably happen if Carl **did not** turn down the heat in the final step?
   - ○ **A.** The stew would be perfect.
   - ○ **B.** It would still take eight hours for the stew to cook.
   - ○ **C.** The giant would no longer be Carl's friend.
   - ◉ **D.** The stew would boil over the pot and make a huge mess.

Information and Study Skills Using an Atlas

**Study the index and the map. Then read each question.
Fill in the circle next to the best answer.**

The United States

Index	
Alabama	J10
Alaska	A1
Arizona	E12
Arkansas	L11
California . . .	B8
Colorado	F6
Connecticut . .	R5
Florida	Q14

Map Grid

1. In which grid square would you look to find Arkansas?
   - **A.** E12
   - **B.** L11
   - **C.** Q14
   - **D.** F6

2. What other state is in the same grid square as Connecticut?
   - **F.** Maine
   - **G.** New Hampshire
   - **H.** Vermont
   - **J.** Rhode Island

3. Part of what state is located in the grid square labeled S5?

- ● **A.** Massachusetts
- ○ **B.** Connecticut
- ○ **C.** New Hampshire
- ○ **D.** Maine

4. What state would you find in grid square B8?

- ● **F.** California
- ○ **G.** Arkansas
- ○ **H.** Colorado
- ○ **J.** Florida

5. What three states are located in the grid square labeled 3R?

- ○ **A.** Connecticut, Massachusetts, Rhode Island
- ○ **B.** Vermont, New Hampshire, Massachusetts
- ● **C.** Vermont, New Hampshire, Maine
- ○ **D.** New Hampshire, Massachusetts, Connecticut

Word Endings *-er* and *-est*

Read each sentence. Choose the correct base word and ending for each underlined word. Fill in the circle next to your answer.

1. The contest was to decide who had the <u>clearest</u> singing voice.
   - ○ **A.** clear + st
   - ◉ **C.** clear + est
   - ○ **B.** clea + rest
   - ○ **D.** cleare + st

2. The pig's voice was <u>smoother</u> than the others' voices.
   - ○ **F.** smoot + her
   - ○ **H.** smoothe + r
   - ◉ **G.** smooth + er
   - ○ **J.** smoo + ther

3. The little mouse had the <u>quietest</u> singing voice.
   - ○ **A.** quie + test
   - ○ **C.** quiet + st
   - ○ **B.** quiete + st
   - ◉ **D.** quiet + est

Read each sentence. Choose the definition of the underlined word. Fill in the circle next to your answer.

4. The horse's voice was <u>louder</u> than the rabbit's voice.
   - ○ **F.** is loud
   - ◉ **G.** more loud
   - ○ **H.** not loud
   - ○ **J.** most loud

5. The owl had the <u>hardest</u> decision in choosing a winner.
   - ◉ **A.** most hard
   - ○ **B.** not hard
   - ○ **C.** was hard
   - ○ **D.** more hard

Name _____

Spelling Vowel + /r/ Sounds

Read each sentence. Then find the correct way to spell the missing word. Fill in the circle next to your answer.

1. The summer day began with a _____, blue sky.

  ○ **A.** cler   ○ **C.** cleer

  ○ **B.** clere   ◉ **D.** clear

2. When the sky suddenly began to _____ dark, Carmen got a very strange feeling.

  ○ **F.** tern   ○ **H.** tirne

  ○ **G.** timre   ◉ **J.** turn

3. Then thousands of frogs _____ to fall from the sky.

  ○ **A.** starded   ○ **C.** stared

  ◉ **B.** started   ○ **D.** startid

4. Carmen crawled under a car and lay in the _____.

  ○ **F.** dirte   ◉ **H.** dirt

  ○ **G.** durt   ○ **J.** dert

5. She waited for the _____ frog rain to end.

  ○ **A.** horrable   ○ **C.** horibull

  ○ **B.** horribel   ◉ **D.** horrible

Name _____

Vocabulary Dictionary: Choosing the Correct Meaning

Study the dictionary entry below. Use the dictionary entry to answer the questions. Fill in the circle next to the best answer.

> **spring** *verb* **1.** To leap in one quick movement: *She sprang from her seat.* **2.** To appear quickly: *New stores seem to spring up every-day.* ◆*noun* **1.** An object made from elastic or soft metal that keeps its original shape after being pulled and twisted. **2.** The act of leaping in one quick movement. **3.** A natural water flow: *The bridge on the trail crossed a spring.* **4.** The time of year between winter and summer.

1. Which is the correct meaning of *spring* in this sentence?
   The stuffed animals <u>spring</u> out of the toy box and onto the floor.
   - ○ **A.** a natural water flow
   - ○ **B.** to appear quickly
   - ○ **C.** the act of leaping in one quick movement
   - ○ **D.** to leap in one quick movement

2. Which is the correct meaning of *spring* in this sentence?
   Bear jumps up and down on a <u>spring</u>.
   - ○ **F.** the act of leaping in one quick movement
   - ○ **G.** to leap in one quick movement
   - ○ **H.** an object made from elastic or soft metal that keeps its original shape after being pulled and twisted
   - ○ **J.** to appear quickly

3. Which is the correct meaning of *spring* in this sentence?

Bear's spring into the air ends with a crash.

- ○ **A.** to appear quickly
- ○ **B.** a natural water flow
- ○ **C.** the time of year between winter and summer
- ◐ **D.** the act of leaping in one quick movement

4. Which is the correct meaning of *spring* in this sentence?

Big lumps spring up on Bear's head.

- ○ **F.** the act of leaping in one quick movement
- ○ **G.** to leap in one quick movement
- ○ **H.** an object made from elastic or soft metal that keeps its original shape after being pulled and twisted
- ◐ **J.** to appear quickly

5. 5. Which is the correct meaning of *spring* in this sentence?

Bear returns to the toy box to sleep until spring.

- ○ **A.** to appear quickly
- ○ **B.** a natural water flow
- ◐ **C.** the time of year between winter and summer
- ○ **D.** the act of leaping in one quick movement

Grammar What Is a Verb?

Find the verb in each sentence. Fill in the circle next to the word you choose.

1. Ava and her mother went to the park for a picnic on the first day of spring.
    - ○ **A.** picnic
    - ● **B.** went
    - ○ **C.** park
    - ○ **D.** mother

2. They sat down on the grass with their picnic basket.
    - ○ **F.** grass
    - ○ **G.** picnic
    - ● **H.** sat
    - ○ **J.** basket

3. Suddenly large snowflakes fell from the clear, blue sky.
    - ○ **A.** rain
    - ● **B.** fell
    - ○ **C.** Suddenly
    - ○ **D.** heavy

4. Ava and her mother fled the park.
    - ○ **F.** park
    - ○ **G.** basket
    - ○ **H.** picnic
    - ● **J.** fled

5. They ate their picnic lunch on the living room floor at home.
    - ○ **A.** floor
    - ○ **B.** room
    - ● **C.** ate
    - ○ **D.** lunch

STOP

Name _____

Writing Skills Using Commas for Direct Address

Read each sentence. Choose the sentence that shows the correct way to use commas. Fill in the circle next to your answer.

1. ○ **A.** Michael, Brad is on the phone for, you.
   ○ **B.** Michael Brad is, on the phone for you.
   ○ **C.** Michael Brad, is on the phone for you.
   ◉ **D.** Michael, Brad is on the phone for you.

2. ○ **F.** Michael, my computer, is acting weird.
   ○ **G.** Michael my computer, is acting weird.
   ◉ **H.** Michael, my computer is acting weird.
   ○ **J.** Michael my computer is acting weird.

3. ○ **A.** I'm sure Brad, that we can solve the problem.
   ○ **B.** I'm sure, Brad that we can solve the problem.
   ◉ **C.** I'm sure, Brad, that we can solve the problem.
   ○ **D.** I'm, sure Brad that we can solve the problem.

4. ◉ **F.** I don't think you understand what's happening, Michael.
○ **G.** I, don't think you understand what's happening Michael.
○ **H.** I don't think, you understand what's happening Michael.
○ **J.** I don't think you understand what's happening Michael.

5. ○ **A.** My computer Michael is drinking soda and eating pizza.
◉ **B.** My computer, Michael, is drinking soda and eating pizza.
○ **C.** My computer, Michael is drinking soda and eating pizza.
○ **D.** My computer Michael, is drinking soda and eating pizza.

Incredible Stories

Level 3, Theme 3: Week 3

Weekly Skills Test Record

Student _____ Date _____

Student Record Form	Possible Score	Criterion Score	Student Score
A: Drawing Conclusions	5	4	
B: Suffixes -*y* and -*ly*	5	4	
C: Spelling /j/, /k/, and /kw/ Sounds	5	4	
D: Vocabulary Dictionary: Pronunciation Key	5	4	
E: Grammar Present Time	5	4	
TOTAL	25	20	
Total Student Score x 4.00 =			%

Name _____

Drawing Conclusions

Read this story. Then read each question. Fill in the circle next to the best answer.

A Royal Mystery

"They're missing again!" yelled Victor. "He has taken our crowns!"

Victor and Virginia ran down the stone stairs. They saw the burn marks on the wall and smelled the melting paintings. The children ran into the great hall. There they found their parents sitting on their thrones.

"Mother, Father, that naughty beast has taken our crowns again," said Virginia. "May we go after him?"

"Yes, you may, but please do be careful," said Mother. "This game gets him so excited that he can't control his hot breath."

Victor looked into the dining hall and said, "He came through here!" The curtains were burned to ashes, chairs were broken, and the long wooden table was burned down the middle and still smoking.

The children followed the trail of burned and broken furniture through one room after another until it ended at two doors. One door led down to the dungeon in the basement. The other led to the kitchen.

"Where do you think he went?" asked Victor. They stood at the doors. Smoke was curling out from around the edges of the dungeon door.

"I think we're about to get those crowns back!" cried Virginia. "Let's go!"

1. Who are Victor and Virginia?
   - ○ **A.** cousins
   - ○ **B.** servants
   - ◉ **C.** brother and sister
   - ○ **D.** friends

2. What information lets you know that Victor and Virginia live in a castle?
   - ○ **F.** There are paintings on the walls.
   - ○ **G.** The stairs are made of stone.
   - ○ **H.** There is a long table in the dining room.
   - ◉ **J.** There are thrones.

3. What information helps you conclude that the beast is friendly?
   - ◉ **A.** He plays games with the children.
   - ○ **B.** He breaks furniture.
   - ○ **C.** He runs away from the children.
   - ○ **D.** He burns curtains.

4. What conclusion can you make about the beast?
   - ○ **F.** He has a tail.
   - ◉ **G.** He breathes fire.
   - ○ **H.** He doesn't like the children.
   - ○ **J.** He's very big in size.

5. How do the children know where the beast is at the end?
   - ○ **A.** They smell melting paintings.
   - ○ **B.** Chairs are broken in the dining hall.
   - ○ **C.** The trail leads them to two doors.
   - ◉ **D.** Smoke is curling out from the dungeon's door.

Suffixes -y and -ly

Read each sentence. Choose the correct base word and ending for each underlined word. Fill in the circle next to your answer.

1. This morning, my sister did not look <u>healthy</u>.
   - ○ **A.** healt + hy
   - ● **C.** health + y
   - ○ **B.** heal + thy
   - ○ **D.** health + ly

2. Her face was <u>completely</u> covered with green polka dots.
   - ● **F.** complete + ly
   - ○ **H.** comple + tely
   - ○ **G.** complet + ely
   - ○ **J.** completel + y

3. My dad said, "We must act <u>quickly</u>."
   - ○ **A.** quickl + y
   - ○ **C.** qui + ckly
   - ● **B.** quick + ly
   - ○ **D.** quic + kly

Read each sentence. Choose the meaning of the underlined word. Fill in the circle next to your answer.

4. He found an old, <u>dusty</u> cookbook and made her some honey pudding.
   - ○ **F.** without dust
   - ○ **H.** most dust
   - ○ **G.** more dust
   - ● **J.** full of dust

5. My sister's face returned <u>slowly</u> to its normal color.
   - ○ **A.** most slow
   - ● **C.** in a slow way
   - ○ **B.** full of slowness
   - ○ **D.** more slow

STOP

Name _____

Spelling /j/, /k/, and /kw/ Sounds

Read each sentence. Then find the correct way to spell the missing word. Fill in the circle next to your answer.

1. Jed woke up feeling _____ and cheerful.
    - ○ **A.** kalm
    - ○ **B.** calm
    - ○ **C.** camme
    - ○ **D.** calme

2. However, when he tried to get dressed, his shirt and _____ ran away from him.
    - ● **F.** jeans
    - ○ **G.** geans
    - ○ **H.** geens
    - ○ **J.** jeens

3. He watched his chair and bed _____ under the door.
    - ● **A.** squeeze
    - ○ **B.** skweeze
    - ○ **C.** sqeeze
    - ○ **D.** scueeze

4. All his toys disappeared in a _____ in the floor.
    - ○ **F.** krak
    - ● **G.** crack
    - ○ **H.** crak
    - ○ **J.** krack

5. All at once, the bedroom became very, very _____.
    - ○ **A.** quit
    - ○ **B.** qwiit
    - ○ **C.** kwiet
    - ● **D.** quiet

Vocabulary Dictionary: Pronunciation Key

Study the pronunciation key, the words, and their pronunciations below. Read each question. Fill in the circle next to the best answer.

ă pat	ĭ pit	oi **oi**l
ā pay	ī ride	o͝o b**oo**k
â care	î f**ie**rce	o͞o b**oo**t
ä father	ŏ pot	ou b**ou**t
ĕ pet	ō go	ŭ cut
ē be	ô p**aw**, f**or**	û fur

spring (sprĭng) **work** (wûrk) **loud** (loud) **chair** (châr) **twice** (twīce)

1. Which word in the pronunciation key shows how to say the vowel sound in *spring?*
   - ○ **A.** pit
   - ○ **B.** father
   - ○ **C.** fierce
   - ○ **D.** pet

2. Which word in the pronunciation key shows how to say the vowel sound in *work?*
   - ○ **F.** care
   - ◐ **G.** fur
   - ○ **H.** for
   - ○ **J.** pot

3. Which word in the pronunciation key shows how to say the vowel sound in *loud?*

   ○ **A.** ride
   ○ **B.** book
   ◉ **C.** bout
   ○ **D.** pay

4. Which word in the pronunciation key shows how to say the vowel sound in *chair?*

   ○ **F.** cut
   ◉ **G.** care
   ○ **H.** father
   ○ **J.** pot

5. Which word in the pronunciation key shows how to say the vowel sound in *twice?*

   ○ **A.** be
   ○ **B.** fierce
   ○ **C.** boot
   ◉ **D.** ride

E Name _____

Grammar Present Time

Read each sentence. Choose the correct verb to complete each sentence. Fill in the circle next to the best answer.

1. When the two sisters _____ the garden, they hear a voice.
   - ◉ **A.** enter
   - ○ **B.** entering
   - ○ **C.** entered
   - ○ **D.** will enter

2. "I _____ a new place to live right now," says the voice.
   - ○ **F.** wanted
   - ◉ **G.** want
   - ○ **H.** wants
   - ○ **J.** wanting

3. The sisters turn and _____ twelve peacocks in a tree.
   - ○ **A.** noticed
   - ○ **B.** notices
   - ◉ **C.** notice
   - ○ **D.** noticing

4. "Too many birds _____ in this tree with me right now!" says one of the peacocks.
   - ○ **F.** lived
   - ◉ **G.** live
   - ○ **H.** will live
   - ○ **J.** lives

5. The sisters _____ around the tree and scare away the other eleven birds.
   - ○ **A.** danced
   - ○ **B.** dancing
   - ○ **C.** dances
   - ◉ **D.** dance

STOP

Incredible Stories

Level 3, Theme 3: Week 4

Weekly Skills Test Record

Student _____   Date _____

Student Record Form

	Possible Score	Criterion Score	Student Score
A: Story Structure	5	4	
B: Information and Study Skills Using Charts, Tables, and Graphs	5	4	
C: Prefixes *un-, bi-, dis-, mis-, and non-*	5	4	
D: Spelling Homophones	5	4	
E: Vocabulary Using a Thesaurus	5	4	
F: Grammar Past Time and Future Time	5	4	
G: Writing Skills Capitalization and Punctuation with Quotations	5	4	
TOTAL	35	28	
Total Student Score x 2.86 =			%

Name _____

Story Structure

Read this story. Then read each question. Fill in the circle next to the best answer.

Good Boy, Tippy

Mr. and Mrs. Shelby patted Tippy's head as they left. "Be a good dog while we're at work," Mrs. Shelby said. "You know the rules. No messes, no getting on the couch, and absolutely no sleeping on our bed." Tippy whined and whimpered. He did not like the rules at all.

The moment the door closed, Tippy trotted to the family room. He jumped on the couch and looked through magazines. When he found a good recipe in one of the magazines, Tippy headed to the kitchen. He pulled out measuring cups and spoons. He climbed all over the counter and dragged ingredients from the cupboards to a big bowl on the floor. Then he stirred up everything he found with his paw and put his creation in the oven.

After the dish was cooked, Tippy put everything back where it belonged. He ate every last crumb and licked up the floor. When he was through, there were no clues left in the kitchen.

Tippy was now so tired and full that he took a nap on the Shelbys' bed. As always, he woke up when he heard the Shelbys' car door close. He quickly smoothed the sheets and jumped down from the bed.

The Shelbys found Tippy sitting quietly by the door just as they did every day. "Now there's my good dog," said Mrs. Shelby.

1. What is the setting of this story?
   ○ **A.** the Shelbys' yard
   ○ **B.** a neighbor's house
   ○ **C.** Mrs. Shelby's office
   ◉ **D.** the Shelbys' house

2. When does the story take place?
   ○ **F.** during one night
   ◉ **G.** during the day
   ○ **H.** during one week
   ○ **J.** during summer

3. What problem does Tippy have?
   ○ **A.** He is bored.
   ◉ **B.** He doesn't like his owners' rules.
   ○ **C.** He sleeps too much.
   ○ **D.** He doesn't like being left alone.

4. How does Tippy solve his problem?
   ○ **F.** He thinks of a game to play.
   ◉ **G.** He breaks the rules, but cleans up so no one can tell.
   ○ **H.** He cooks for his owners.
   ○ **J.** He waits quietly for his owners to return.

5. How does the story end?
   ○ **A.** Mrs. Shelby reminds Tippy of the rules.
   ○ **B.** The Shelbys return to a messy house.
   ◉ **C.** The Shelbys find Tippy sitting by the door.
   ○ **D.** Tippy eats the food that he made.

B Name _____

Information and Study Skills:
Using Charts, Tables, and Graphs

Study the graph. Then read each question. Fill in the circle next to the best answer.

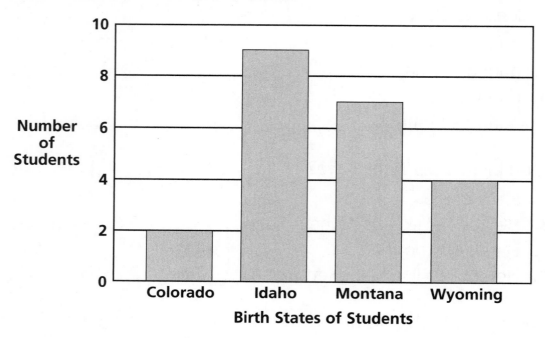

1. In which state were four students born?
   - ○ **A.** Wyoming
   - ○ **B.** Idaho
   - ○ **C.** Colorado
   - ○ **D.** Montana

2. In which state were the fewest students born?
   - ○ **F.** Wyoming
   - ○ **G.** Idaho
   - ○ **H.** Colorado
   - ○ **J.** Montana

Go on ⇨

3. In which states were more than five students born?
   - ○ **A.** Wyoming and Colorado
   - ○ **B.** Idaho and Wyoming
   - ○ **C.** Montana and Colorado
   - ◐ **D.** Montana and Idaho

4. In which states were nine students born?
   - ○ **F.** Idaho and Wyoming
   - ○ **G.** Wyoming and Montana
   - ◐ **H.** Montana and Colorado
   - ○ **J.** Idaho and Montana

5. How many students were born in Montana and Wyoming?
   - ○ **A.** ten
   - ○ **B.** thirteen
   - ○ **C.** twelve
   - ◐ **D.** eleven

Prefixes *un-*, *bi-*, *dis-*, *mis-*, and *non-*

Read each sentence. Choose the correct word to complete each sentence. Fill in the circle next to your answer.

1. "You never eat when I tell you to! Why do you always _____ me?" Anna asked her dog Shadow.
   - ○ **A.** disable
   - ◉ **C.** disobey
   - ○ **B.** unlock
   - ○ **D.** recover

2. Shadow put down the newspaper and looked up at her through his _____. "It's only dry dog food that I don't eat."
   - ○ **F.** bicycle
   - ○ **H.** discovery
   - ○ **G.** unfair
   - ◉ **J.** bifocals

3. "I didn't know. I was completely _____," said Anna.
   - ○ **A.** unhappy
   - ○ **C.** unbroken
   - ◉ **B.** unaware
   - ○ **D.** nonsense

4. "What happened?" she asked. "You used to eat it _____, all the time."
   - ○ **F.** uncertain
   - ◉ **H.** nonstop
   - ○ **G.** unclear
   - ○ **J.** nonsense

5. "I discovered that the label doesn't say what's in the food. I _____ food when I don't know what's in it," said Shadow.
   - ◉ **A.** mistrust
   - ○ **C.** refill
   - ○ **B.** dishonest
   - ○ **D.** mistake

STOP

D Name _____

Spelling Homophones

Read each sentence. Then find the correct way to spell the missing word. Fill in the circle next to your answer.

1. Pablo _____ something was wrong when a purple cloud filled his bedroom.
   - ○ **A.** new
   - ◉ **C.** knew
   - ○ **B.** nue
   - ○ **D.** knoo

2. A _____ in black armor appeared in the cloud.
   - ○ **F.** nite
   - ◉ **H.** knight
   - ○ **G.** night
   - ○ **J.** knite

3. His fierce _____ had wings.
   - ○ **A.** hoarse
   - ◉ **C.** horse
   - ○ **B.** hors
   - ○ **D.** horss

4. Pablo realized he was about to _____.
   - ○ **F.** deye
   - ○ **H.** digh
   - ○ **G.** dye
   - ◉ **J.** die

5. "Do not be frightened, for I come in _____," said the man.
   - ◉ **A.** peace
   - ○ **C.** peece
   - ○ **B.** peesse
   - ○ **D.** piece

E Name _____

Vocabulary Using a Thesaurus

Study the thesaurus entry below. Read each sentence. Choose the best word to replace the word *hit*. Fill in the circle next to your answer.

> **hit,** slap, pound, punch, smash, kick. All of these verbs can mean "to touch something very hard."

1. Mike tried to smack the giant killer bee with the palm of his hand. He <u>hit</u> his own forehead instead.
   - ○ **A.** smashed
   - ◉ **B.** slapped
   - ○ **C.** punched
   - ○ **D.** kicked

2. Mike made a fist to <u>hit</u> the giant killer bee. The bee flew through a window into the house where Hannah was still asleep.
   - ○ **F.** slap
   - ○ **G.** kick
   - ○ **H.** pound
   - ◉ **J.** punch

3. Mike tried to open the front door but it was locked. Mike <u>hit</u> the door with his fists.

   ○ **A.** pounded
   ○ **B.** slapped
   ○ **C.** kicked
   ○ **D.** punched

4. Mike <u>hit</u> the door with his foot.

   ○ **F.** kicked
   ○ **G.** pounded
   ○ **H.** punched
   ○ **J.** smashed

5. Hannah suddenly pulled open the door. The door accidentally <u>hit</u> the killer bee. Her life was saved.

   ○ **A.** kicked
   ○ **B.** punched
   ○ **C.** slapped
   ○ **D.** smashed

Grammar Past Time and Future Time

Read each sentence. Choose the correct verb to complete each sentence. Fill in the circle next to the best answer.

1. As the twins walked in the garden, a voice _____, "Get me out of here!"
   - ● **A.** screamed
   - ○ **B.** will scream
   - ○ **C.** scream
   - ○ **D.** screaming

2. The twins went over and _____ behind the trees and bushes.
   - ○ **F.** look
   - ○ **G.** looking
   - ○ **H.** looks
   - ● **J.** looked

3. "I _____ you in silver coins tomorrow for a new place to live today," said the voice.
   - ○ **A.** paying
   - ○ **B.** paid
   - ● **C.** will pay
   - ○ **D.** pays

4. Then the twins _____ a peacock in a rotting tree.
   - ● **F.** noticed
   - ○ **G.** noticing
   - ○ **H.** notices
   - ○ **J.** will notice

5. "We _____ for a new home tomorrow if you pay us today," said the twins.
   - ○ **A.** searched
   - ● **B.** will search
   - ○ **C.** searches
   - ○ **D.** search

STOP

Name _____

Writing Skills Capitalization and Punctuation with Quotations

Read each sentence. Choose the sentence that has the correct punctuation and capitalization. Fill in the circle next to your answer.

1. ○ **A.** "Please come over right away." Brad said, "something weird is happening."
    ○ **B.** "Please come over right away," Brad said something weird is happening.
    ○ **C.** "Please come over right away" Brad said. "Something weird is happening."
    ◔ **D.** "Please come over right away," Brad said. "Something weird is happening."

2. ○ **F.** Michael said. "I'll be right over."
    ◔ **G.** Michael said, "I'll be right over."
    ○ **H.** Michael said, i'll be right over.
    ○ **J.** Michael said "I'll be right over."

3. ○ **A.** When a strange woman opened the door to Brad's house. Michael asked, "Where's Brad?"
    ◔ **B.** When a strange woman opened the door to Brad's house, Michael asked, "Where's Brad?"
    ○ **C.** When a strange woman opened the door to Brad's house, Michael asked, "where's Brad?"
    ○ **D.** When a strange woman opened the door to Brad's house, Michael asked. "Where's Brad?"

Go on ⇨

4. 🔘 **F.** "I'm sorry," the woman at the door said. "No one named Brad lives here."

⚪ **G.** "I'm sorry" The woman at the door said, "No one named Brad lives here."

⚪ **H.** "I'm sorry," the woman at the door said "no one named Brad lives here."

⚪ **J.** I'm sorry, the woman at the door said. "No one named Brad lives here."

5. ⚪ **A.** "but that can't be!," said Michael. "I live in the house next door."

⚪ **B.** "But that can't be!" said Michael "I live in the house next door."

⚪ **C.** "But that can't be!" Said Michael. "I live in the house next door."

🔘 **D.** "But that can't be!" said Michael. "I live in the house next door."

STOP

Animal Habitats

Level 3, Theme 4: Week 1

Weekly Skills Test Record

Student _____ Date _____

Student Record Form

	Possible Score	Criterion Score	Student Score
A: Fact and Opinion	5	4	
B: Information and Study Skills Multimedia Resources	5	4	
C: Syllabication	5	4	
D: Spelling Vowel + *r* Sound in *hair*	5	4	
E: Vocabulary Dictionary: Parts of Speech	5	4	
F: Grammar Verb *be*	5	4	
TOTAL	30	24	
Total Student Score x 3.33 =			%

Fact and Opinion

Read this story. Then read each question. Fill in the circle next to the best answer.

Behaving Like an Animal

Have you ever seen a squirrel or a rat? How about a nutria? Nutrias are rodents, which puts them in the same category as squirrels, rats, and even beavers. They are cute animals that have brown fur and long tails.

People brought nutrias to Europe and North America from South America. They hoped to raise nutrias for their fur. Yet, this was not a smart idea. Not enough money was made from nutrias' fur, so the people gave up. Nutrias, however, learned how to survive in their new homelands.

Unfortunately, nutrias have become real pests in many places. They cause leaks in dams by digging holes. They eat so many water plants that other animals starve. Nutrias can even destroy crops of rice and sugar cane.

Because they are so cute, people think nutrias are harmless. Yet, these animals are a very big problem. Many people don't want them around anymore.

1. Which of the following statements gives an opinion?
   - ○ **A.** Nutrias have brown fur.
   - ◉ **B.** Nutrias are cute.
   - ○ **C.** Nutrias are rodents.
   - ○ **D.** Nutrias came from South America.

2. Which of these states a fact?
- ○ **F.** Nutrias are cute.
- ○ **G.** Raising nutrias for their fur is not a smart idea.
- ○ **H.** Nutrias are a problem.
- ◉ **J.** Nutrias can destroy crops of rice and sugar cane.

3. Which word tells you that this statement gives an opinion?

People think nutrias look harmless.
- ◉ **A.** think
- ○ **B.** people
- ○ **C.** harmless
- ○ **D.** look

4. How can you tell that this statement tells a fact?

These animals cause leaks in dams by digging holes.
- ○ **F.** It is written by the author.
- ◉ **G.** You can ask people who take care of dams if this is true.
- ○ **H.** Everyone knows that when a dam has a hole, it leaks.
- ○ **J.** It isn't a fact.

5. Which of these statements shows the author's opinion about nutrias?
- ○ **A.** Nutrias are rodents.
- ○ **B.** Nutrias learned how to survive.
- ◉ **C.** Nutrias are a very big problem.
- ○ **D.** Nutrias can even destroy crops of rice.

Information and Study Skills
Multimedia Resources

Read each question. Then fill in the circle next to the best answer.

1. What should you keep in mind when you do research on the Internet?
   - ○ **A.** The information may not always be correct.
   - ○ **B.** The Internet gives too much information.
   - ○ **C.** The Internet is only made up of opinions.
   - ○ **D.** Using the Internet is the best way to do research.

2. Once you find an Internet search engine to use, what should you do?
   - ○ **F.** Compare the information to an encyclopedia.
   - ○ **G.** Click on the list of sites that appears on the screen.
   - ○ **H.** Type in a useful keyword.
   - ○ **J.** Start your search over.

3. Which is the best topic to search under to find out what polar bears eat?
   - ○ **A.** food
   - ○ **B.** polar bears
   - ○ **C.** animals
   - ○ **D.** animal health

Go on ⇨

4. In searching the Internet for information on polar bears, which related topic are you likely to come across?

○ **F.** cold weather clothes

○ **G.** snow games

○ **H.** weather

◉ **J.** grizzly bears

5. How are electronic encyclopedias different from the Internet?

○ **A.** The Internet is always faster.

◉ **B.** Information in encyclopedias is usually correct.

○ **C.** Topics can only be used for an Internet search.

○ **D.** The "Search" feature works only with encyclopedias.

Syllabication

Read each sentence. Then choose the best way to divide each underlined word into syllables. Fill in the circle next to the best answer.

1. Leo and Maria went on a hike into the <u>wilderness</u>.
   - ○ **A.** wi • lde • rness
   - ● **C.** wil • der • ness
   - ○ **B.** wil • dern • ess
   - ○ **D.** wild • ern • ess

2. They were <u>looking</u> for wildlife.
   - ○ **F.** lo • oking
   - ○ **H.** loo • king
   - ● **G.** look • ing
   - ○ **J.** l • ook • ing

Choose the best word to complete each sentence. Fill in the circle next to your answer.

3. Leo heard a loud and _____ noise like a knock.
   - ○ **A.** confusion
   - ○ **C.** confused
   - ○ **B.** confuse
   - ● **D.** confusing

4. "That's the beak of a _____ hitting a tree," said Maria.
   - ○ **F.** wooded
   - ● **H.** woodpecker
   - ○ **G.** wooden
   - ○ **J.** woodwork

5. "It must be _____ a hole for its nest," she said.
   - ● **A.** creating
   - ○ **C.** create
   - ○ **B.** creation
   - ○ **D.** created

STOP

Name _____

Spelling Vowel + *r* Sound in *hair*

Read each sentence. Then find the correct way to spell the missing word. Fill in the circle next to your answer.

1. Scott and his dad spotted a grizzly _____ near the river.
- ○ **A.** bare
- ◉ **C.** bear
- ○ **B.** bere
- ○ **D.** bair

2. "It's very _____ to see a grizzly near here," said his dad.
- ○ **F.** rear
- ○ **H.** rair
- ◉ **G.** rare
- ○ **J.** raire

3. After she caught a _____ of salmon, the grizzly lifted her head toward Scott and his dad.
- ○ **A.** pear
- ○ **C.** pere
- ◉ **B.** pair
- ○ **D.** paire

4. "We _____ not stay here any longer," said Scott's dad.
- ○ **F.** dair
- ○ **H.** dahre
- ○ **G.** dear
- ◉ **J.** dare

5. "That gave me quite a _____," said Scott as he and his dad drove away.
- ◉ **A.** scare
- ○ **C.** scair
- ○ **B.** scear
- ○ **D.** scayre

Name _____

Vocabulary Dictionary: Parts of Speech

Study the dictionary entry below. Read the question. Fill in the circle next to the best answer.

fly[1] *verb* **1.** To move over air using wings: *Not every bird can fly.*
2. To move through air in an aircraft: *I flew to Idaho to see my sister.* **3.** In baseball, to hit a ball high in the air: *He flew out to centerfield to end the game.* **4.** To move quickly: *Summertime always seems to fly by.* ◆ *noun* **1.** In baseball, a ball hit high in the air. **2.** A flap of cloth that covers a zipper.
fly[1] (flī) ◆ *verb* **flew** or **flied** (for sense 3), **flown** or **flied** (for sense 3), **flying** ◆ *noun, plural* **flies**

fly[2] *noun* An insect with wings, especially one in the group that includes the housefly.
fly[2] (flī) ◆ *noun, plural* **flies**

Which part of speech is *fly* in each sentence?

1. *One day I was in my home town, catching <u>flies</u> in center field.*
   - ○ **A.** a verb
   - ○ **B.** a plural
   - ○ **C.** a guide word
   - ◑ **D.** a noun

2. *The next day I was in Africa watching a leopard <u>fly</u> by so fast that I couldn't get a picture of it.*
   - ○ **F.** an adjective
   - ○ **G.** a pronunciation
   - ◑ **H.** a verb
   - ○ **J.** a noun

3. *Throughout our tour of Africa, we were bothered by <u>flies</u> buzzing around us.*
- ○ **A.** a base word
- ○ **B.** an adverb
- ○ **C.** a verb
- ◉ **D.** a noun

4. *There were so many bugs that I just wished they would all <u>fly</u> away.*
- ○ **F.** a plural
- ◉ **G.** a verb
- ○ **H.** an adjective
- ○ **J.** a noun

5. *I always made sure to close the <u>fly</u> of my sleeping bag at night.*
- ○ **A.** a definition
- ○ **B.** a verb
- ◉ **C.** an noun
- ○ **D.** a plural

Name _____

Grammar Verb *be*

Read each group of sentences. Choose the sentence that is written correctly. Fill in the circle next to the best answer.

1. ○ **A.** I is very interested in whales.
    ◉ **B.** I am very interested in whales.
    ○ **C.** I are very interested in whales.
    ○ **D.** I were very interested in whales.

2. ○ **F.** My brother are also interested in whales.
    ○ **G.** My brother were also interested in whales.
    ○ **H.** My brother am also interested in whales.
    ◉ **J.** My brother is also interested in whales.

3. ◉ **A.** Last summer was very exciting.
    ○ **B.** Last summer are very exciting.
    ○ **C.** Last summer is very exciting.
    ○ **D.** Last summer were very exciting.

4. ◉ **F.** I was with my brother and my dad on a trip.
    ○ **G.** I were with my brother and my dad on a trip.
    ○ **H.** I is with my brother and my dad on a trip.
    ○ **J.** I are with my brother and my dad on a trip.

5. ○ **A.** We am on a boat to watch whales.
    ○ **B.** We is on a boat to watch whales.
    ◉ **C.** We were on a boat to watch whales.
    ○ **D.** We was on a boat to watch whales.

Animal Habitats

Level 3, Theme 4: Week 2

Weekly Skills Test Record

Student _____ Date _____

Student Record Form	Possible Score	Criterion Score	Student Score
A: Compare and Contrast	5	4	
B: Word Endings -ed and -ing and Changing Final y to i	5	4	
C: Spelling Added Endings	5	4	
D: Vocabulary Dictionary: More Multiple-Meaning Words	5	4	
E: Grammar Helping Verbs	5	4	
TOTAL	25	20	
Total Student Score x 4.00 =			%

Name _____

Compare and Contrast

Read this passage. Then read each question. Fill in the circle next to the best answer.

Crocodiles and Alligators

Can you tell a crocodile from an alligator? They are alike in some ways. Yet, in other ways, they are very different.

Both animals are covered with scales and have backbones. They have short legs and long, powerful tails. Also, baby crocodiles and alligators both hatch from eggs.

Both crocodiles and alligators are very dangerous and very strong hunters. Both eat fish and small animals, and they can even attack people, though that is rare. These two animals have strong jaws and many sharp teeth. They also have eyes high on their head so they can see while they float in the water. Both can be found in hot, damp places like swamps.

Crocodiles and alligators are different in certain ways. For example, a crocodile's snout, or the part of its head that sticks outward and includes its nose and mouth, is pointed at the end. The snout of an alligator is broad and rounder. Also, crocodiles like muddy, shallow water, while alligators are usually found in deeper water.

1. Which is true about both crocodiles and alligators?
   - ○ **A.** They have backbones.
   - ○ **B.** Their eyes are set low on the sides of their heads.
   - ○ **C.** They cannot float on water.
   - ○ **D.** They live in deep water.

2. How is a crocodile's body different from an alligator's?
- ○ **F.** Crocodiles have short legs.
- ○ **G.** Crocodiles have a short tail.
- ○ **H.** Crocodiles have sharper teeth.
- ◉ **J.** Crocodiles have pointed snouts.

3. How are crocodiles and alligators alike?
- ○ **A.** They both like to attack people.
- ◉ **B.** Their bodies are covered with scales.
- ○ **C.** They have only a couple of sharp teeth.
- ○ **D.** They only eat fish.

4. How are crocodiles and alligators different?
- ○ **F.** Only crocodiles eat small animals.
- ○ **G.** Only alligators have strong jaws.
- ◉ **H.** Only alligators have rounded snouts.
- ○ **J.** Only crocodiles live in water.

5. What do alligators do that crocodiles do not?
- ○ **A.** live in hot, damp places
- ○ **B.** lay eggs
- ◉ **C.** live in deeper water
- ○ **D.** eat fish

B Name _____

Word Endings *-ed* and *-ing* and Changing Final *y* to *i*

Read each sentence. Choose the base word and ending for each underlined word. Fill in the circle next to the best answer.

1. Our class was <u>studying</u> all about birds.
   - ● **A.** study + ing
   - ○ **B.** studi + ing
   - ○ **C.** stud + ing
   - ○ **D.** stud + yng

2. We were <u>invited</u> to the local zoo by the zookeeper.
   - ○ **F.** invit + ed
   - ● **G.** invite + ed
   - ○ **H.** invite + d
   - ○ **J.** invit + ted

3. While we looked around, we spotted a flock of geese <u>flying</u> over the zoo.
   - ● **A.** fly + ing
   - ○ **B.** fli + ing
   - ○ **C.** fly + ng
   - ○ **D.** fli + ying

4. Suddenly, we <u>noticed</u> an injured goose on the ground.
   - ○ **F.** notice + d
   - ○ **G.** notic + ed
   - ○ **H.** noti + ced
   - ● **J.** notice + ed

5. Our teacher <u>hurried</u> to find the zookeeper.
   - ○ **A.** hurrie + d
   - ○ **B.** hurr + yed
   - ● **C.** hurry + ed
   - ○ **D.** hurri + ed

STOP

Name _____

Spelling Added Endings

Read each sentence. Then find the correct way to spell the missing word. Fill in the circle next to your answer.

1. Scott told Mom about how he and Dad _____ from the grizzly.
   - ○ **A.** escapped
   - ○ **B.** escapied
   - ○ **C.** escapeed
   - ◉ **D.** escaped

2. "I wonder why the grizzly _____ towards us," said Scott.
   - ○ **F.** steped
   - ○ **G.** stepied
   - ◉ **H.** stepped
   - ○ **J.** stepid

3. "She was _____ for her cubs," said Dad.
   - ◉ **A.** caring
   - ○ **B.** carring
   - ○ **C.** carrin
   - ○ **D.** carrinng

4. "Oh, I didn't see her _____," said Scott.
   - ○ **F.** babees
   - ○ **G.** babyes
   - ○ **H.** babbies
   - ◉ **J.** babies

5. "She'd do anything to protect her children," said Mom _____.
   - ○ **A.** smilling
   - ◉ **B.** smiling
   - ○ **C.** smilin
   - ○ **D.** smilinng

Name _____

Vocabulary Dictionary: More Multiple-Meaning Words

Study the dictionary entry below. Use the dictionary entry to answer the questions. Fill in the circle next to the best answer.

fly¹ *verb* **1.** To move over air using wings: *Not every bird can fly.* **2.** To move through air in an aircraft: *I flew to Idaho to see my sister.* **3.** In baseball, to hit a ball high in the air: *He flew out to centerfield to end the game.* **4.** To move quickly: *Summertime always seems to fly by.* ◆ *noun* **1.** In baseball, a ball hit high in the air. **2.** A flap of cloth that covers a zipper.
fly¹ (flī) ◆ *verb* **flew** or **flied** (for sense 3), **flown** or **flied** (for sense 3), **flying** ◆ *noun, plural* **flies**

fly² *noun* An insect with wings, especially one in the group that includes the housefly.
fly² (flī) ◆ *noun, plural* **flies**

What is the meaning of *fly* in each sentence?

1. *We saw many birds during our trip, even some that couldn't fly.*
- ○ **A.** To move through air in an aircraft
- ○ **B.** A flap of cloth that covers a zipper
- ◉ **C.** To move over air using wings
- ○ **D.** To move quickly

2. *We were in such a rugged part of the country that we had to*
   fly in by helicopter.
   - ● **F.** To move through air in an aircraft
   - ○ **G.** To move quickly
   - ○ **H.** An insect with wings, especially one in the group that includes the housefly
   - ○ **J.** In baseball, to hit a ball high in the air

3. *At night it was so cold that I had to close the fly on my sleeping*
   bag to keep the air from going through the zipper.
   - ○ **A.** In baseball, a ball hit high in the air
   - ● **B.** A flap of cloth that covers a zipper
   - ○ **C.** To move over air using wings
   - ○ **D.** To move through air in an aircraft

4. *During the night, I dreamt of hitting a fly over the fielder's*
   head to win the game.
   - ○ **F.** To move quickly
   - ○ **G.** An insect with wings, especially one in the group that includes the housefly
   - ○ **H.** In baseball, to hit a ball high in the air
   - ● **J.** In baseball, a ball hit high in the air

5. *Because the trip was so much fun, the time just flew by.*
   - ○ **A.** To move through air in an aircraft
   - ○ **B.** A flap of cloth that covers a zipper
   - ○ **C.** To move over air using wings
   - ● **D.** To move quickly

Grammar Helping Verbs

Read each sentence. Choose the answer that best completes the sentence. Fill in the circle next to the correct answer.

1. "My brother _____ whales before," I told the boat captain.
    - ○ **A.** has watched
    - ○ **B.** have watch
    - ○ **C.** have watched
    - ○ **D.** has watch

2. "So he _____ to me that I must be patient," I said.
    - ○ **F.** have explained
    - ○ **G.** have explain
    - ◉ **H.** has explained
    - ○ **J.** has explain

3. "But we _____ for over two hours without seeing a whale," I complained.
    - ○ **A.** has traveled
    - ○ **B.** have traveled
    - ○ **C.** has travel
    - ○ **D.** have travel

4. "I _____ whales in this area many times," said the boat captain.
    - ○ **F.** has seen
    - ○ **G.** have saw
    - ◉ **H.** have seen
    - ○ **J.** has saw

5. "Look," my brother shouted, "a whale _____!"
    - ○ **A.** have arrived
    - ○ **B.** has arrived
    - ○ **C.** has arrive
    - ○ **D.** have arrive

(STOP)

Animal Habitats

Level 3, Theme 4: Week 3
Weekly Skills Test Record

Student _____ Date _____

Student Record Form	Possible Score	Criterion Score	Student Score
A: Making Judgments	5	4	
B: Prefixes *un-*, *re-* and Suffixes *-ful*, *-ly*, *-er*	5	4	
C: Spelling Prefixes and Suffixes	5	4	
D: Vocabulary Dictionary: Base Words and Inflected Forms	5	4	
E: Grammar Irregular Verbs	5	4	
F: Writing Skills Varying Sentence Types	5	4	
TOTAL	30	24	
Total Student Score x 3.33 =			%

Name _____

Making Judgments

Read this passage. Then read each question. Fill in the circle next to the best answer.

Sidewalk Rescue

Toby and Elena were just beginning their walk home from school. "Look!" said Toby. "There's a baby bird on the side-walk!"

"Do you see how it's trying to flap its wings?" asked Elena. "Maybe its mother is teaching it how to fly." The children turned in circles looking for the bird's mother, but there were no other birds around.

"Hey, there's the nest!" Toby called out. He pointed to a small clump of grass and twigs in a nearby bush. "I think we should put the bird back in its nest," he said.

Elena frowned. "I don't think that's a good idea. Baby birds are not very strong. What if you hurt it?"

"If I don't move it, its mother may not find it," said Toby.

"Just stay here and watch it. I'll go get a teacher to help us." Elena headed toward the school building.

As Toby was deciding what to do, he noticed a cat watching from across the street. It quietly moved closer and closer as it stared at the tiny bird. "I can't just leave the bird here on the sidewalk," Toby thought. "It's too dangerous."

Toby wrapped his hands in his scarf and gently picked up the helpless bird as the cat ran toward it. Toby placed the bird in the nest, and the cat stopped at the bush, looked up at the nest, and licked its lips. "Don't worry, little bird," said Toby. "You're safe now."

1. What do Toby and Elena disagree about?
   - ○ **A.** whether to move the bird's nest
   - ○ **B.** who the cat belongs to
   - ○ **C.** how to find the missing mother bird
   - ● **D.** how to help the baby bird

2. What is good about Toby's solution?
   - ○ **F.** It will show the baby bird how to fly.
   - ○ **G.** It might hurt the bird.
   - ● **H.** It will keep the bird out of danger.
   - ○ **J.** It will make the mother bird return.

3. Why might Elena's idea to get an adult's help be best?
   - ○ **A.** An adult can scare the cat away.
   - ○ **B.** Adults are not afraid of animals.
   - ● **C.** An adult may know how to handle the bird.
   - ○ **D.** An adult can teach the bird to fly.

4. What might be bad about Toby's idea?
   - ○ **F.** Elena might not come back.
   - ● **G.** Toby might hurt the bird.
   - ○ **H.** Toby might not find the nest.
   - ○ **J.** The bird might fly away.

5. What might be bad about Elena's idea?
   - ○ **A.** The teacher might not believe Elena.
   - ○ **B.** The baby bird might fly away before Elena comes back.
   - ● **C.** The cat might get the bird before Elena returns with an adult.
   - ○ **D.** Toby might hurt the bird.

STOP

Name _____

Prefixes *un-*, *re-* and Suffixes *-ful*, *-ly*, *-er*

Read each sentence. Then find the meaning of each underlined word. Fill in the circle next to the best answer.

1. Mr. Lansing was a wheat <u>farmer</u>.
    - ○ **A.** full of farming
    - ○ **B.** farm again
    - ○ **C.** the opposite of farm
    - ◉ **D.** one who farms

2. He planned to clean his shed and <u>rearrange</u> his tools.
    - ○ **F.** the opposite of arrange
    - ◉ **G.** arrange again
    - ○ **H.** in an arranged way
    - ○ **J.** full of arranging

3. He found an <u>untidy</u> pile of rags and paper in a corner.
    - ○ **A.** in a tidy way
    - ○ **B.** tidy again
    - ○ **C.** full of tidy
    - ◉ **D.** not tidy

4. When he moved the pile, several mice <u>hurriedly</u> scampered away.
    - ◉ **F.** in a hurried way
    - ○ **G.** the opposite of hurried
    - ○ **H.** hurried again
    - ○ **J.** one who hurries

5. The farmer was <u>careful</u> to patch all the holes he could find.
    - ○ **A.** one who cares
    - ○ **B.** caring again
    - ◉ **C.** full of care
    - ○ **D.** the opposite of care

Name _____

Spelling Prefixes and Suffixes

Read each sentence. Then find the correct way to spell the missing word. Fill in the circle next to your answer.

1. The forest ranger and her _____, Diana, watched the grizzly turn toward them.
    - ○ **A.** helpir
    - ○ **B.** helpper
    - ○ **C.** helpere
    - ◉ **D.** helper

2. "That grizzly doesn't look too _____," said the ranger.
    - ○ **F.** friendlie
    - ○ **G.** friendley
    - ◉ **H.** friendly
    - ○ **J.** frendly

5. "Maybe she will change her mind," said Diana, but she didn't sound very _____.
    - ○ **A.** hopful
    - ◉ **B.** hopeful
    - ○ **C.** hopefully
    - ○ **D.** hopefull

4.   When the grizzly decided to <wol> to her cubs, the ranger and Diana were relieved.
    - ○ **F.** reeturn
    - ◉ **G.** return
    - ○ **H.** retern
    - ○ **J.** returne

5. "I'm glad we are both _____," said the ranger.
    - ○ **A.** unnhurt
    - ◉ **B.** unhurt
    - ○ **C.** inhurt
    - ○ **D.** enhurt

Vocabulary Dictionary: Base Words and Inflected Forms

Study the dictionary entry below. Read the question. Fill in the circle next to the best answer.

fly[1] *verb* **1.** To move over air using wings: *Not every bird can fly.* **2.** To move through air in an aircraft: *I flew to Idaho to see my sister.* **3.** In baseball, to hit a ball high in the air: *He flew out to centerfield to end the game.* **4.** To move quickly: *Summertime always seems to fly by.* ♦ *noun* **1.** In baseball, a ball hit high in the air. **2.** A flap of cloth that covers a zipper.
fly[1] (flī) ♦ *verb* **flew** or **flied** (for sense 3), **flown** or **flied** (for sense 3), **flying** ♦ *noun, plural* **flies**

fly[2] *noun* An insect with wings, especially one in the group that includes the housefly.
fly[2] (flī) ♦ *noun, plural* **flies**

Which form of *fly* best completes each sentence?

1. *"I dreamt that I kept dropping _____ to center field."*
   ○ **A.** flew
   ○ **B.** fly
   ○ **C.** flown
   ◉ **D.** flies

Go on

2. *"I woke up with all these _____ buzzing around my head."*
- ● **F.** flies
- ○ **G.** flown
- ○ **H.** fly
- ○ **J.** flew

3. *"The time _____ by as we drove to the small airport."*
- ○ **A.** flies
- ○ **B.** fly
- ○ **C.** flown
- ● **D.** flew

4. *"So how big was the plane _____ home?" my friend asked.*
- ○ **F.** flied
- ○ **G.** flies
- ● **H.** flying
- ○ **J.** flew

5. *"It was tiny. And we saw many birds _____ by the window!"*
- ○ **A.** flown
- ● **B.** fly
- ○ **C.** flied
- ○ **D.** flew

Grammar Irregular Verbs

Read each sentence. Choose the answer that best completes the sentence. Fill in the circle next to the correct answer.

1. I _____ that I would never see a whale.
   - ○ **A.** thinked
   - ◉ **B.** thought
   - ○ **C.** had thinked
   - ○ **D.** has thought

2. Suddenly, something large and dark _____ up out of the water.
   - ◉ **F.** came
   - ○ **G.** come
   - ○ **H.** had came
   - ○ **J.** come

3. My brother _____ the whale before anyone else.
   - ○ **A.** have seen
   - ○ **B.** seen
   - ○ **C.** had saw
   - ◉ **D.** saw

4. My father _____ me the binoculars.
   - ○ **F.** have gaved
   - ◉ **G.** gave
   - ○ **H.** has gived
   - ○ **J.** given

5. Right then, I knew I _____ the best vacation ever.
   - ○ **A.** had took
   - ○ **B.** have take
   - ◉ **C.** had taken
   - ○ **D.** had take

STOP

Name _____

Writing Skills Varying Sentence Types

Read each question. Fill in the circle next to the best answer.

1. How could you change this sentence to a command?

Can you see the baby deer across the meadow?

- ○ **A.** Do you see the baby deer across the meadow?
- ○ **B.** There is a baby deer across the meadow.
- ○ **C.** What a beautiful baby deer!
- ◉ **D.** Look at the baby deer across the meadow.

2. How could you change this sentence to a question?

I wonder if you can see the fawn's mother.

- ○ **F.** I do not see the fawn's mother.
- ○ **G.** Find the fawn's mother.
- ◉ **H.** Can you see the fawn's mother?
- ○ **J.** What a lonely fawn with no mother!

3. How could you change this sentence to an exclamation?

I see a buck with large antlers.

- ◉ **A.** What large antlers that buck has!
- ○ **B.** Have you ever seen such large antlers?
- ○ **C.** Those are very large antlers.
- ○ **D.** Look at that buck's antlers.

 Go on

4. How could you change this sentence to a statement?

Do you hear that rustling noise?

- ○ **F.** What is that rustling noise?
- ○ **G.** What a strange noise that is!
- ◉ **H.** I think I hear a rustling noise.
- ○ **J.** Listen to that rustling noise.

5. How could you change this sentence to a command?

The deer run very gracefully.

- ○ **A.** Have you ever seen animals run more gracefully?
- ◉ **B.** Watch how gracefully the deer run.
- ○ **C.** I think the deer run very gracefully.
- ○ **D.** How gracefully the deer run!

Voyagers

Level 3, Theme 5: Week 1

Weekly Skills Test Record

Student _____   Date _____

Student Record Form

	Possible Score	Criterion Score	Student Score
A: Making Inferences	5	4	
B: Suffixes -less and -ness	5	4	
C: Spelling Vowel Sounds in tooth and cook	5	4	
D: Vocabulary Dictionary: Syllables	5	4	
E: Grammar Subject Pronouns	5	4	
TOTAL	25	20	
Total Student Score x 4.00 =			%

Making Inferences

Read this story. Then read each question. Fill in the circle next to the best answer.

A First-Time Traveler

Debbie was about to fly on an airplane for the first time. She frowned as she watched the big planes land and take off. She was trying to imagine how it would feel to leave the ground where it was safe. Debbie stepped a little closer to her father.

"You're squeezing my hand pretty tightly," he said with a smile.

Finally, it was time to board the plane. As they walked down the crowded aisle of the airplane, Debbie lost hold of her father's hand. "Dad, wait for me!"

Her father reached back and took her hand. "Don't worry. I'm right here." They walked past three more rows. "Here are our seats. Would you like to sit by the window?"

Debbie sat by the window and clenched her fists tightly. She kept her eyes closed while the plane took off. After they were in the air, she opened her eyes. The ride was very smooth. It felt just like riding in a car. She looked out the window and saw buildings, roads, and farms through the clouds. It was fun to see how small things looked. Debbie rested back against her seat and smiled at her father.

He gave her a wink and squeezed her hand. "Grandma will be very glad to see you."

"Maybe we could fly out to see her every summer," said Debbie.

1. Which is a clue that shows how Debbie feels while waiting to board the plane?
   - ◉ **A.** She is frowning.
   - ○ **B.** She watches the planes take off.
   - ○ **C.** She stands near her father.
   - ○ **D.** She holds her father's hand.

2. Which word best describes how Debbie feels at the beginning of the story?
   - ○ **F.** happy
   - ○ **G.** bored
   - ◉ **H.** worried
   - ○ **J.** dreamy

3. Which is a clue that shows how Debbie feels as the plane takes off?
   - ○ **A.** She sits by the window.
   - ◉ **B.** She clenches her fists and keeps her eyes closed.
   - ○ **C.** She sits next to her father.
   - ○ **D.** She doesn't get out of her seat.

4. Which clue best shows how Debbie's feelings about flying changed?
   - ◉ **F.** She wants to fly to her Grandma's every summer.
   - ○ **G.** She opens her eyes after takeoff.
   - ○ **H.** She looks out the window at the view.
   - ○ **J.** She wants her father to wait for her.

5. Which word best describes how Debbie feels at the end of the story?
   - ○ **A.** worried
   - ○ **B.** bored
   - ○ **C.** upset
   - ◉ **D.** relaxed

STOP

Suffixes *-less* and *-ness*

Read each sentence. Then choose the correct base word and ending for each underlined word. Fill in the circle next to the best answer.

1. The divers shone a light through the <u>darkness</u> of the deep ocean.
   - ○ **A.** dare + kness
   - ● **B.** dark + ness
   - ○ **C.** dar + kness
   - ○ **D.** darkn + ess

2. Long ago, a <u>careless</u> captain had run his ship against the rocks.
   - ○ **F.** car + less
   - ● **G.** care + less
   - ○ **H.** carele + ss
   - ○ **J.** car + eless

Read each sentence. Then choose the correct word that stands for the underlined words. Fill in the circle next to the best answer.

3. Many thought it was <u>without use</u> to look for the old ship.
   - ○ **A.** useful
   - ○ **B.** used
   - ● **C.** useless
   - ○ **D.** using

4. One day, the divers' <u>condition of being stubborn</u> finally paid off.
   - ● **F.** stubbornness
   - ○ **G.** stubbornly
   - ○ **H.** stubbornnless
   - ○ **J.** stubborn

5. They found the ship and its <u>without price</u> treasure.
   - ○ **A.** pricing
   - ○ **B.** priced
   - ● **C.** priceless
   - ○ **D.** pricey

STOP

Name _____

Spelling Vowel Sounds in *tooth* and *cook*

**Read each sentence. Then find the correct way to
spell the missing word. Fill in the circle next to
your answer.**

1. Ms. Dooley and her daughter traveled in a hot air _____.
    - ● **A.** balloon
    - ○ **C.** ballewn
    - ○ **B.** ballune
    - ○ **D.** baloon

2. "Everything _____ so pretty from up here," said her daughter.
    - ○ **F.** lokes
    - ○ **H.** luks
    - ● **G.** looks
    - ○ **J.** loeks

3. They _____ over farms and towns.
    - ○ **A.** floo
    - ○ **C.** floe
    - ○ **B.** flue
    - ● **D.** flew

4. Things went smoothly until the skies _____ dark and windy.
    - ○ **F.** groo
    - ● **H.** grew
    - ○ **G.** groe
    - ○ **J.** grue

5. The two travelers had to land in a farmer's field near some _____.
    - ○ **A.** wouds
    - ○ **C.** wodes
    - ○ **B.** woulds
    - ● **D.** woods

Name _____

Vocabulary Dictionary: Syllables

Study the dictionary entries below. Read each question. Fill in the circle next to the best answer.

> **explorer** *noun* Someone who explores an unknown place.
> **ex•plor•er** (ĭk **splôr′**ər) ◆ *noun, plural* **explorers**
>
> **sailor** *noun* Someone who sails, often as a member of the crew of a ship.
> **sail•or** (sā′ lər) ◆ *noun, plural* **sailors**
>
> **traveler** *noun* Someone who goes on a trip.
> **trav•el•er** (trăv′əl ər) ◆ *noun, plural* **travelers**

1. How many syllables does *sailor* have?
   - ○ **A.** one
   - ◉ **B.** two
   - ○ **C.** three
   - ○ **D.** four

2. How many syllables does *explorer* have?
   - ○ **F.** one
   - ○ **G.** two
   - ◉ **H.** three
   - ○ **J.** four

3. How many syllables does *traveler* have?

- ○ **A.** one
- ◉ **B.** two
- ◉ **C.** three
- ○ **D.** four

4. Which is the second syllable of *explorer*?

- ○ **F.** ex
- ○ **G.** plo
- ◉ **H.** plor
- ○ **J.** er

5. Which is the first syllable of *traveler*?

- ○ **A.** vel
- ○ **B.** tra
- ○ **C.** travel
- ◉ **D.** trav

Name _____

Grammar Subject Pronouns

Read each sentence. Choose the word that correctly replaces the underlined word or phrase in each sentence. Fill in the circle next to the answer you choose.

1. <u>My mother and I</u> and I are going to Canada this summer.
   - ○ **A.** Us
   - ◉ **B.** We
   - ○ **C.** Me
   - ○ **D.** They

2. We can't wait to see Canada. <u>Canada</u> is a very interesting country.
   - ◉ **F.** It
   - ○ **G.** We
   - ○ **H.** He
   - ○ **J.** Him

3. My mother was born in Canada. <u>My mother</u> is glad we will visit there.
   - ○ **A.** He
   - ◉ **B.** She
   - ○ **C.** They
   - ○ **D.** Her

4. We will be staying with my Uncle Henry and his family.
   <u>Uncle Henry and his family</u> live in an old farm house.
   - ○ **F.** Us
   - ○ **G.** Them
   - ◉ **H.** They
   - ○ **J.** He

5. <u>Uncle Henry</u> is going to take us up to the mountains.
   - ◉ **A.** He
   - ○ **B.** They
   - ○ **C.** Him
   - ○ **D.** It

Voyagers

Level 3, Theme 5: Week 2
Weekly Skills Test Record

Student _____ Date _____

Student Record Form	Possible Score	Criterion Score	Student Score
A: Predicting Outcomes	5	4	
B: Possessives	5	4	
C: Spelling Vowel Sound in *bought*	5	4	
D: Vocabulary Analogies	5	4	
E: Grammar Object Pronouns	5	4	
TOTAL	25	20	
Total Student Score x 4.00 =			%

Name _____

Predicting Outcomes

Read the story. Then read each question and fill in the circle next to the best answer.

Sailing for Home

Lee was a quiet man who did things his own way. Rather than working at an office job like many of his friends, Lee became an artist. He also loved to read about other cultures. Yet, later in his life, Lee felt tired and bored, as if he wasn't doing and seeing as much as he could. So, at the age of fifty-seven, Lee bought a boat and set sail for New Zealand from Seattle, Washington.

When he was almost halfway to New Zealand, Lee dropped anchor off the coast of a tiny island in the Pacific Ocean. He swam to shore, and the people there greeted him with warmth, smiles, and a party that lasted all night. Lee hadn't expected this and wasn't prepared for such a warm greeting. He wanted to show respect for the people's customs, so he joined in their fun. He danced and danced even though he was exhausted from the trip.

Four weeks later into his journey, Lee began to run very low on food. He fished for his supper and almost always was successful. Though he went hungry only a few times, he was still very uneasy not knowing when he might catch his next meal.

Lee finally arrived in New Zealand five months after leaving Seattle. Though happy he had made the trip, he felt it would be too difficult to return home by boat. So he placed an ad in a newspaper to try to sell the boat. Meanwhile, he lived on the boat and put fresh paint on it, but it didn't sell. Lee finally bought a plane ticket for home, leaving the boat behind. He had been away from home for almost one year. It was time to go back.

Go on ⇨

1. What is Lee likely to do before he goes on another long sailing trip?
   - ○ **A.** learn how to fish
   - ◉ **B.** bring enough food
   - ○ **C.** invite a friend along
   - ○ **D.** study the weather maps more closely

2. If Lee decides to visit another unfamiliar place, what is he likely to do before he leaves home?
   - ○ **F.** pack pictures of his home
   - ○ **G.** finish a painting to bring as a gift
   - ○ **H.** buy a gift
   - ◉ **J.** study the customs of the people

3. If the islanders had asked Lee to help them finish building a hut, what do you think Lee would have done?
   - ○ **A.** laughed at the idea
   - ○ **B.** swum back to his boat
   - ◉ **C.** helped them
   - ○ **D.** asked them for money

4. Which detail is important for predicting Lee's future actions?
   - ○ **F.** He swims to the island.
   - ○ **G.** He fishes for his supper.
   - ○ **H.** He flies back to Seattle.
   - ◉ **J.** He respects other people's ways of life.

5. If Lee needed to sell another boat, what might he do differently?
   - ○ **A.** put fresh paint on the boat first
   - ◉ **B.** place the ad in more than one place
   - ○ **C.** sail the boat to New Zealand
   - ○ **D.** buy a plane ticket

STOP

Name _____

Possessives

Read each sentence. Then find the possessive that correctly replaces the underlined part of the sentence. Fill in the circle next to the best answer.

1. The dream that my dad had was to sail all the way to Mexico.
   - ◉ **A.** My dad's dream
   - ○ **C.** My dads' dream
   - ○ **B.** The dream's dad
   - ○ **D.** My dads dream

2. It was an idea my mother had to take the whole family on the trip.
   - ○ **F.** my mothers idea
   - ○ **H.** my mothers' idea
   - ◉ **G.** my mother's idea
   - ○ **J.** my moth'ers idea

3. The eyes of my brothers got very big when they heard the plan.
   - ○ **A.** My brothers eye's
   - ○ **C.** My brother's eyes
   - ○ **B.** My brothers eyes
   - ◉ **D.** My brothers' eyes

4. The smiles of my sisters made it clear that both girls loved the idea.
   - ○ **F.** My sister's smiles
   - ○ **H.** My sisters smile's
   - ◉ **G.** My sisters' smiles
   - ○ **J.** My sisters smiles

5. I couldn't wait for the big adventure of my family.
   - ○ **A.** my familys' big adventure
   - ○ **B.** my families big adventure
   - ◉ **C.** my family's big adventure
   - ○ **D.** my families' big adventure

Name _____

Spelling Vowel Sound in *bought*

**Read each sentence. Then find the correct way to
spell the missing word. Fill in the circle next to
your answer.**

1. Mr. Cooper took his son and his _____ on an overnight
camping trip.

    ○ **A.** doughter   ◉ **C.** daughter
    ○ **B.** dawghter   ○ **D.** dawter

2. The Coopers _____ enough food and water for two days.

    ○ **F.** braht   ○ **H.** brawt
    ◉ **G.** brought   ○ **J.** braught

3. They _____ that they were going to leave in the morning.

    ○ **A.** thawt   ◉ **C.** thought
    ○ **B.** thaught   ○ **D.** thauht

4. But they were _____ in a heavy rain storm and had to stay an
extra night.

    ○ **F.** cawt   ◉ **H.** caught
    ○ **G.** cought   ○ **J.** caht

5. This trip _____ the children to always be prepared.

    ○ **A.** tawght   ○ **C.** tught
    ○ **B.** tought   ◉ **D.** taught

Vocabulary Analogies

Read each sentence. Find the word that correctly completes the sentence. Fill in the circle next to your answer.

1. <u>Ship</u> is to <u>water</u> as <u>bus</u> is to _____.
   - ● **A.** land
   - ○ **B.** air
   - ○ **C.** driver
   - ○ **D.** car

2. <u>Track</u> is to <u>train</u> as <u>road</u> is to _____.
   - ○ **F.** home
   - ● **G.** car
   - ○ **H.** helicopter
   - ○ **J.** street

3. <u>Near</u> is to <u>far</u> as <u>small</u> is to _____.
   - ○ **A.** little
   - ○ **B.** size
   - ○ **C.** short
   - ● **D.** large

Go on ⇨

4. Suitcase is to traveler as backpack is to _____.

   ○ **F.** doctor

   ○ **G.** artist

   ◉ **H.** hiker

   ○ **J.** sleeping bag

5. Airplane is to pilot as boat is to _____.

   ◉ **A.** captain

   ○ **B.** ocean

   ○ **C.** passenger

   ○ **D.** flyer

Name _____

Grammar Object Pronouns

Read each sentence. Choose the word that correctly replaces the underlined word or phrase in each sentence. Fill in the circle next to the answer you choose.

1. My scout troop is going to Canada again and this time I am going with <u>the troop</u>.
    - ○ **A.** him
    - ● **C.** it
    - ○ **B.** us
    - ○ **D.** you

2. Some of our parents are going with <u>my troop and me</u>.
    - ○ **F.** it
    - ○ **H.** them
    - ○ **G.** we
    - ● **J.** us

3. My little sister asked me to send lots of postcards to <u>my little sister</u>.
    - ○ **A.** us
    - ● **C.** her
    - ○ **B.** him
    - ○ **D.** she

4. We have been writing to Canadian pen pals and will get to meet <u>our pen pals</u>.
    - ○ **F.** us
    - ● **H.** them
    - ○ **G.** him
    - ○ **J.** you

5. Mr. Fox will drive the van, and Mr. Costa will help <u>Mr. Fox</u>.
    - ● **A.** him
    - ○ **C.** them
    - ○ **B.** he
    - ○ **D.** you

STOP

Voyagers

Level 3, Theme 5: Week 3

Weekly Skills Test Record

Student _____ Date _____

Student Record Form	Possible Score	Criterion Score	Student Score
A: Text Organization	5	4	
B: Information and Study Skills Using a Time Line	5	4	
C: VCCV Pattern	5	4	
D: Spelling VCCV Pattern	5	4	
E: Vocabulary Homophones	5	4	
F: Grammar Possessive Pronouns	5	4	
G: Writing Skills Writing Dates and Times	5	4	
TOTAL	35	28	
Total Student Score x 2.86 =			%

Name _____

Text Organization

Read this passage. Then read each question. Fill in the circle next to the best answer.

Sailing Ships of Long Ago

People have been sailing for thousands of years. The boats that were built varied in size and purpose.

Greek Ships

The Greeks built large warships that used sails and a line of rowers along each side to move the ship. The warships had a large, sharp point on the front. The point was used to ram other boats in battle.

Greek Warship

Roman Ships

The Romans had the largest fleet of working ships in ancient times. They built many huge ships for carrying grain. These ships could carry about a thousand tons of grain and a thousand passengers at once.

Roman Grain Ship

Ships of the Vikings

The Vikings were among the best boat builders of their time. Their strong crafts, called long ships, carried the Vikings across the Atlantic to Greenland and North America. The Vikings were proud of their fine ships.

Viking Long Ship

Go on

1. Which of these is a heading used in the article?
   - ○ **A.** Working Ships
   - ○ **B.** Greek Warship
   - ◉ **C.** Roman Ships
   - ○ **D.** Sailing Ships of Long Ago

2. Which is a caption for an illustration in the article?
   - ○ **F.** Sailing Ships of Long Ago
   - ◉ **G.** Viking Long Ship
   - ○ **H.** Roman Ships
   - ○ **J.** Greek Ships

3. Which feature in the article helps the reader understand the difference between the ships?
   - ○ **A.** introduction
   - ○ **B.** title
   - ○ **C.** captions
   - ◉ **D.** illustrations

4. What is the purpose of the text next to each illustration?
   - ○ **F.** to show what the ships looked like
   - ○ **G.** to explain the differences among the ships
   - ○ **H.** to name the ship
   - ◉ **J.** to explain how the ships were used

5. Which feature could have been included to help organize the information?
   - ○ **A.** a concluding paragraph that describes modern ships
   - ○ **B.** more illustrations
   - ◉ **C.** the dates the ships were in use
   - ○ **D.** the name of each boat pictured

STOP

Name _____

Information and Study Skills
Using a Time Line

**Study the time line below. Then read each question.
Fill in the circle next to the best answer.**

Events of Columbus's First Voyage

August 3, 1492 — Columbus's ships, *Niña*, *Pinta*, and *Santa Maria*, leave Spain.

The sailors threaten to turn back.

October 10, 1492

October 12, 1492 — The sailors see land and Columbus goes ashore. He names the island San Salvador.

December 25, 1492 — The *Santa Maria* is wrecked near Haiti.

January 16, 1493 — The *Niña* and *Pinta* begin the journey back to Spain.

February 14, 1493 — The ships become separated during a nighttime storm.

March 15, 1493 — The *Niña* arrives at Palos, Spain. The *Pinta* arrives later the same day.

Go on ⟶

1. In which month did more than one event happen?
   - ○ **A.** August, 1492
   - ◉ **B.** October, 1492
   - ○ **C.** January, 1493
   - ○ **D.** February, 1493

2. Which happened before Columbus found San Salvador?
   - ○ **F.** The *Pinta* arrived in Spain.
   - ○ **G.** The *Niña* and *Pinta* became separated during a storm.
   - ◉ **H.** The crew threatened to turn back.
   - ○ **J.** The *Niña* and *Pinta* began the journey back to Spain.

3. When was the *Santa Maria* wrecked?
   - ○ **A.** October 12, 1492
   - ◉ **B.** December 25, 1492
   - ○ **C.** January 16, 1493
   - ○ **D.** March 15, 1493

4. What happened during February, 1493?
   - ○ **F.** Columbus left Spain.
   - ○ **G.** The sailors saw land.
   - ○ **H.** The *Niña* arrived in Spain.
   - ◉ **J.** The *Niña* and the *Pinta* became separated during a storm.

5. How long did it take the *Niña* and *Pinta* to return to Spain?
   - ◉ **A.** two months
   - ○ **B.** four months
   - ○ **C.** six months
   - ○ **D.** one year

VCCV Pattern

Read each sentence. Then find the correct way to divide the underlined word into syllables. Fill in the circle next to the best answer.

1. Teresa and her family were on a very special <u>journey</u>.
   - ○ **A.** journ • ey
   - ○ **B.** jou • rney
   - ○ **C.** jo • ur • ney
   - ◉ **D.** jour • ney

2. They were riding on one of the first steam <u>engine</u> trains.
   - ◉ **F.** en • gine
   - ○ **G.** e • ngine
   - ○ **H.** engi • ne
   - ○ **J.** eng • ine

3. On the train, they could travel a great <u>distance</u> in one day.
   - ○ **A.** dist • ance
   - ○ **B.** di • stance
   - ◉ **C.** dis • tance
   - ○ **D.** distan • ce

4. Teresa smiled as she looked out the <u>window</u> of the train.
   - ○ **F.** wi • ndow
   - ○ **G.** wind • ow
   - ○ **H.** wi • n • dow
   - ◉ **J.** win • dow

5. She fell asleep <u>wondering</u> who lived in the homes they passed.
   - ○ **A.** won • dering
   - ◉ **B.** won • der • ing
   - ○ **C.** wond • er • ing
   - ○ **D.** wonder • ing

STOP

Name _____

Spelling VCCV Pattern

Read each sentence. Then find the correct way to spell the missing word. Fill in the circle next to your answer.

1. At last the canoe trip was going to happen!
   - ○ **A.** hapin
   - ○ **C.** hapen
   - ○ **B.** happin
   - ◉ **D.** happen

2. Ms. Dooley and her son and daughter started the trip early _____ morning.
   - ○ **F.** Monnday
   - ◉ **H.** Monday
   - ○ **G.** Munday
   - ○ **J.** Mounday

3. Ms. Dooley had not been expecting the _____ storm.
   - ◉ **A.** sudden
   - ○ **C.** sudin
   - ○ **B.** suden
   - ○ **D.** suddin

4. She and her children were a little scared _____ they reached the shore.
   - ○ **F.** untill
   - ◉ **H.** until
   - ○ **G.** unntil
   - ○ **J.** uhntil

5. "That was a trip we'll never _____!" said the children.
   - ○ **A.** forghet
   - ○ **C.** forgett
   - ○ **B.** forrget
   - ◉ **D.** forget

E Name _____

Vocabulary Homophones

Read each sentence. Find the word that correctly completes the sentence. Fill in the circle next to your answer.

1. Boat builders use the _____ of many trees to build a strong ship.
   - ○ **A.** would
   - ◉ **B.** wood
   - ○ **C.** blue
   - ○ **D.** blew

2. The _____ of a ship must be made of strong cloth.
   - ○ **F.** meat
   - ○ **G.** meet
   - ◉ **H.** sails
   - ○ **J.** sales

3. A ship must be strong to travel safely _____ storms.
   - ○ **A.** bare
   - ○ **B.** bear
   - ○ **C.** threw
   - ◉ **D.** through

Go on ⇨

4. Sometimes a ship is tossed about on a stormy _____.

  ○ **F.** see
  ◉ **G.** sea
  ○ **H.** knot
  ○ **J.** not

5. It takes only one _____ part to make a ship unsafe.

  ◉ **A.** weak
  ○ **B.** week
  ○ **C.** right
  ○ **D.** write

Grammar Possessive Pronouns

Read each sentence. Choose the phrase that correctly replaces the underlined phrase in each sentence. Fill in the circle next to the answer you choose.

1. Did you ever go on a long trip with <u>the friends you have</u>?
- ○ **A.** your friends
- ○ **B.** her friends
- ○ **C.** our friends
- ○ **D.** their friends

2. I am going on a camping trip with <u>the friends that I have</u>.
- ○ **F.** we friends
- ○ **G.** their friends
- ○ **H.** her friends
- ○ **J.** my friends

3. My brother is letting me use <u>the camping gear that belongs to my brother</u>.
- ○ **A.** us camping gear
- ○ **B.** their camping gear
- ○ **C.** his camping gear
- ○ **D.** our camping gear

Go on

4. Both my parents are taking <u>vacation time that belongs to them</u> to go on the trip.

- ○ **F.** our vacation time
- ◐ **G.** their vacation time
- ○ **H.** we vacation time
- ○ **J.** my vacation time

5. We are going to keep a diary of <u>the places that are favorites to us</u>.

- ○ **A.** their favorite places
- ◐ **B.** our favorite places
- ○ **C.** his favorite places
- ○ **D.** we favorite places

Writing Skills Writing Dates and Times

Read each group of sentences. Choose the correct date or time that replaces the underlined words. Fill in the circle next to the answer you choose.

1. The <u>fourteenth of June in 2000</u> was one of my favorite days.
    ○ **A.** June, 14, 2000   ○ **C.** June, 14 2000
    ○ **B.** June 14 2000   ◉ **D.** June 14, 2000

2. We left New York at <u>seven thirty in the morning</u>.
    ○ **F.** 7:30 A.M   ◉ **H.** 7:30 A.M.
    ○ **G.** 7:30 AM   ○ **J.** 730 AM.

3. Our plane landed in Berlin, Germany, at <u>six forty-five in the evening</u>.
    ◉ **A.** 6:45 P.M.   ○ **C.** 6:45 PM.
    ○ **B.** 6:45 PM   ○ **D.** 645 P.M.

4. When we got to Germany it was <u>eleven o'clock at night</u>.
    ○ **F.** 1100 P.M.   ○ **H.** 11,00 PM
    ◉ **G.** 11:00 P.M.   ○ **J.** 11:00 P:M

5. We stayed in Germany until the <u>second of July in 2000</u>.
    ○ **A.** July 2/2000   ○ **C.** July/2/2000
    ○ **B.** July, 2 2000   ◉ **D.** July 2, 2000

STOP

Smart Solutions

Level 3, Theme 6: Week 1

Weekly Skills Test Record

Student _____ Date _____

Student Record Form	Possible Score	Criterion Score	Student Score
A: Problem Solving and Decision Making	5	4	
B: VCCCV Pattern	5	4	
C: Spelling Words Ending with *-er* or *-le*	5	4	
D: Vocabulary Dictionary: Synonyms	5	4	
E: Grammar Adjectives	5	4	
TOTAL	25	20	
Total Student Score x 4.00 =			%

Name _____

Problem Solving and Decision Making

Read this story. Then read each question. Fill in the circle next to the best answer.

A New Friend

Charlotte had been in her new school for over a month and had not made any friends.

"Charlotte," said Ms. Taylor, "if you would talk to the other students, they'd be your friends." But when other students invited her to join their work group, Charlotte just shook her head and worked by herself. She wanted to make friends, but she was simply too shy.

One day there was another new student in the class. His name was Ed. The new boy sat at the empty desk next to Charlotte. When the teacher introduced Ed to the class, she used sign language while she spoke. Ed watched carefully. When Ms. Taylor told Ed that she was happy to have him in the class, he made the sign for *thank you*. He put one hand flat against his mouth then moved it away and placed it flat against his other hand. His lips said "Thank you," but he did not make a sound.

When Ed sat down, he waved at Charlotte and his lips said "Hi." Charlotte waved back shyly. Ed took a book out of his pack and handed it to Charlotte. The book showed the hand signs for words and letters. Charlotte smiled and made the same sign for *thank you* that Ed had made earlier. She wrote a note and passed it to Ed.

Ed read the note and grinned. He moved his lips and signed, "Yes, you can be my friend. Can I be yours?"

1. What problem does Charlotte have?
   - ○ **A.** The other students are mean to her.
   - ○ **B.** Her teacher does not notice her.
   - ◉ **C.** She is too shy to make friends.
   - ○ **D.** She doesn't like the other students.

2. How is her problem solved?
   - ◉ **F.** She writes a note to Ed, asking to be his friend.
   - ○ **G.** Her classmates ask her to join in the work group.
   - ○ **H.** She waves hello to Ed.
   - ○ **J.** Ed sits next to Charlotte.

3. What is a reason to think that Charlotte's solution is a good one?
   - ○ **A.** She will now feel comfortable talking to the other students.
   - ○ **B.** Charlotte can now join others in group work.
   - ○ **C.** Charlotte can feel comfortable with the other students.
   - ◉ **D.** She and Ed are both new students who can help each other.

4. What is a reason to think that Charlotte's decision is a poor one?
   - ○ **F.** She has to learn sign language.
   - ◉ **G.** She still doesn't have to talk.
   - ○ **H.** She'll be called on more often in class.
   - ○ **J.** She'll still be alone.

5. What other way could Charlotte have successfully solved her problem?
   - ○ **A.** written down everything she wanted to say
   - ○ **B.** sent a letter to her teacher
   - ◉ **C.** joined one of the children's work groups
   - ○ **D.** asked her father to let her stay at home

STOP

VCCCV Pattern

Read each sentence. Then choose the best way to divide each underlined word into syllables. Fill in the circle next to your answer.

1. Sometimes my baby brother Sammy gets out of <u>control</u>.
   - ○ **A.** contr • ol
   - ○ **B.** cont • rol
   - ○ **C.** con • tr • ol
   - ◉ **D.** con • trol

2. He tried to <u>improve</u> the model of the solar system I made.
   - ○ **F.** imp • rove
   - ○ **G.** i • mpr • ove
   - ◉ **H.** im • prove
   - ○ **J.** imp • ro • ve

3. Sammy looked like a huge <u>monster</u> tearing apart the planets.
   - ◉ **A.** mon • ster
   - ○ **B.** mons • ter
   - ○ **C.** mon • st • er
   - ○ **D.** monst • er

4. <u>Instead</u> of getting mad, I just had to laugh.
   - ○ **F.** Ins • tead
   - ○ **G.** In • ste • ad
   - ○ **H.** Inst • ead
   - ◉ **J.** In • stead

5. I can never stay <u>angry</u> at him because he's too young to know better.
   - ○ **A.** a • ngr • y
   - ◉ **B.** an • gry
   - ○ **C.** angr • y
   - ○ **D.** an • gr • y

STOP

Name _____

Spelling Words Ending with *-er* or *-le*

Read each sentence. Then find the correct way to spell the missing word. Fill in the circle next to your answer.

1. Every _____ I have the same problem.
   - ○ **A.** summir
   - ◉ **C.** summer
   - ○ **B.** sumer
   - ○ **D.** summar

2. My best friend Max goes to camp, but I am not _____ to go.
   - ○ **F.** abel
   - ○ **H.** abele
   - ◉ **G.** able
   - ○ **J.** abell

3. I go with my family to visit my _____ and cousins in France.
   - ○ **A.** unkel
   - ○ **C.** unkell
   - ◉ **B.** uncle
   - ○ **D.** unkle

4. Almost every day we _____ someplace and have a picnic.
   - ○ **F.** bicycal
   - ○ **H.** bicycul
   - ○ **G.** bicykale
   - ◉ **J.** bicycle

5. At night I e-mail Max on the _____ to tell him about our trip.
   - ○ **A.** computor
   - ◉ **C.** computer
   - ○ **B.** computere
   - ○ **D.** computar

Name _____

Vocabulary Dictionary: Synonyms

Read each sentence. Then choose the word that means the same or nearly the same as the underlined word. Fill in the circle next to the best answer.

1. Nancy felt <u>unsure</u> that she would do well on her test.
   - ○ **A.** certain
   - ○ **B.** confident
   - ○ **C.** weak
   - ◉ **D.** doubtful

2. Then her sister gave her a big hug and told her to <u>stop</u> worrying.
   - ○ **F.** start
   - ◉ **G.** halt
   - ○ **H.** create
   - ○ **J.** begin

3. Immediately, Nancy felt <u>calm</u>.
   - ◉ **A.** relaxed
   - ○ **B.** tense
   - ○ **C.** firm
   - ○ **D.** mean

4. During the test, all the students worked <u>silently</u>.
   - ○ **F.** noisily
   - ◉ **G.** quietly
   - ○ **H.** hard
   - ○ **J.** thoughtfully

5. Nancy was <u>thrilled</u> when she received a high grade on her test.
   - ◉ **A.** delighted
   - ○ **B.** ashamed
   - ○ **C.** quiet
   - ○ **D.** puzzled

STOP

Name _____

Grammar Adjectives

Read each sentence. Find the word that correctly completes the sentence. Fill in the circle next to your answer.

1. Allen's class was going on _____ field trip to a farm.
   - ◉ **A.** a
   - ○ **B.** an
   - ○ **C.** tasty
   - ○ **D.** few

2. He made sure that he packed _____ oranges on the kitchen counter.
   - ○ **F.** a
   - ○ **G.** an
   - ◉ **H.** the
   - ○ **J.** few

3. Allen found _____ open seat next to Jack on the bus.
   - ◉ **A.** an
   - ○ **B.** a
   - ○ **C.** some
   - ○ **D.** two

4. It took a _____ time to reach the farm.
   - ◉ **F.** long
   - ○ **G.** one
   - ○ **H.** happy
   - ○ **J.** the

5. Allen couldn't wait to eat his _____ oranges.
   - ○ **A.** one
   - ◉ **B.** two
   - ○ **C.** the
   - ○ **D.** easy

Smart Solutions

Level 3, Theme 6: Week 2
Weekly Skills Test Record

Student _____ Date _____

Student Record Form	**Possible Score**	**Criterion Score**	**Student Score**
A: Drawing Conclusions	5	4	
B: Information and Study Skills Following Directions	5	4	
C: VCV Pattern	5	4	
D: Spelling Words Beginning with *a* or *be*	5	4	
E: Vocabulary Dictionary: Antonyms	5	4	
F: Grammar Comparing with Adjectives	5	4	
TOTAL	30	24	
		Total Student Score x 3.33 =	**%**

Name _____

Drawing Conclusions

Read this passage. Then read each question. Fill in the circle next to the best answer.

A Close Call

Scott smiled as he headed downstairs. It was his mother's special day, and he had hidden her gift in a box behind some bags in the basement. Scott had saved his allowance for six weeks. Then he had gone to his mother's favorite department store and asked the clerk to help him pick out a necklace. He even paid to have the necklace gift-wrapped. He couldn't wait to see his mother's face when she opened the beautiful present.

Scott went to the corner where the gift was hidden. But where were all the bags of old clothes? Scott looked all around. He was very worried and upset.

"Mom!" he called up the stairs. "Where are the bags of clothes that were down here?"

"Oh, that old junk? I had your father take them to the thrift store," she answered. "There are some rags in the laundry room if you're cleaning your bike."

Scott ran to the garage and hopped on his bike. He rode as fast as he could toward the thrift store. He was only halfway there when he saw his father driving toward home. It was too late. Scott felt like crying.

Scott's father pulled over and called, "Hey, Scott! Do you know anything about this?" He held up a long, thin, velvet box.

Scott grinned with relief. "I sure do, Dad. I sure do."

1. On what day does this story most likely take place?
   - ○ **A.** Mother's Day
   - ○ **B.** Fourth of July
   - ○ **C.** Thanksgiving
   - ○ **D.** Valentine's Day

2. What detail leads you to conclude what day it is?
   - ○ **F.** Scott bought a necklace.
   - ○ **G.** It was his mother's special day.
   - ○ **H.** Scott's father had the box.
   - ○ **J.** Scott was worried when he couldn't find the box.

3. Why does Scott feel like crying when he sees his father driving home?
   - ○ **A.** Scott was lost.
   - ○ **B.** He was relieved that he found his father.
   - ○ **C.** He thought the necklace had been given away.
   - ○ **D.** His dad didn't stop.

4. Why does Scott smile when his father shows him the box?
   - ○ **F.** He realizes the necklace is safe.
   - ○ **G.** Scott thinks the box has a gift for him in it.
   - ○ **H.** It's his father's gift to his mother.
   - ○ **J.** It's a pretty box.

5. What detail about the box supports your conclusion about why Scott grins?
   - ○ **A.** It's made of velvet.
   - ○ **B.** It's long and thin like a necklace.
   - ○ **C.** It's the size that a watch could fit in.
   - ○ **D.** It looks like it holds jewelry that his father might have bought.

STOP

Information and Study Skills
Following Directions

Read this passage. Then read each question. Fill in the circle next to the best answer.

Smart Saver Piggy Bank

Do you spend your allowance the moment you get it? Try making this piggy bank and filling it up. You'll be surprised by what you can buy with your savings!

Collect the following items before you start. You'll need a two-liter plastic soda bottle with a cap screwed on, tape, three small cardboard tubes, many strips of newspaper, and a pair of scissors. Also, get two cups of flour, two cups of water, and a large bowl from the kitchen. Lastly, you'll need a pipe cleaner, some craft paint, and paint brushes.

To begin, cut two of the cardboard tubes in half to make the legs. Cut triangles out of the other tube for the ears. Attach all of these pieces to the bottle with tape. Next, stick the pipe cleaner into the end of the bottle. Curl the pipe cleaner so it looks like a pig's tail. Next, mix the flour and water in the large bowl until they form a smooth paste. After you've made the paste, dip the newspaper strips into it. Place the newspaper strips over the soda bottle, the legs, the ears, and the tail.

Leave the pig to dry overnight. The next day, paint your piggy bank with your favorite colors. Finally, ask an adult for help cutting the slot where you will put your money.

Congratulations, you've made a piggy bank! Whenever you have change in your pockets, you can put it in your bank. When the pig is full, you can buy yourself something special!

1. Which is something you need for making the piggy bank?
   - ○ **A.** buttons
   - ○ **B.** paper plates
   - ○ **C.** felt
   - ● **D.** a soda bottle

2. Why should you cut and attach the legs **before** you paste on the newspaper strips?
   - ○ **F.** so the pieces will not get lost
   - ○ **G.** so the paint will dry faster
   - ● **H.** so the newspaper will cover over the tubes
   - ○ **J.** so the slot can be cut into the bottle more easily

3. What is the next step **after** placing the newspaper strips on the pig's body?
   - ● **A.** Leave the bottle to dry overnight.
   - ○ **B.** Paint it.
   - ○ **C.** Mix the flour and water into a paste.
   - ○ **D.** Collect the rest of the materials.

4. At what point should you ask for an adult's help?
   - ○ **F.** when gathering materials
   - ● **G.** when cutting the slot for the money
   - ○ **H.** when mixing the paste
   - ○ **J.** when covering the pig in newspaper strips

5. How long will it take to make this piggy bank?
   - ○ **A.** about an hour
   - ○ **B.** half a day
   - ○ **C.** two hours
   - ● **D.** more than one day

(STOP)

Name _____

VCV Pattern

Read each sentence. Then choose the best way to divide each underlined word into syllables. Fill in the circle next to your answer.

1. My dad almost missed our <u>vacation</u>.
    - ● **A.** va • ca • tion
    - ○ **B.** vac • at • ion
    - ○ **C.** vaca • tion
    - ○ **D.** va • cation

2. Something was wrong with the <u>motor</u> of his car.
    - ○ **F.** mot • or
    - ● **G.** mo • tor
    - ○ **H.** mo • t • or
    - ○ **J.** mo • to • r

3. We were to meet at the airport and <u>travel</u> to Florida.
    - ● **A.** trav • el
    - ○ **B.** tra • vel
    - ○ **C.** trave • l
    - ○ **D.** tra • ve • l

4. When the <u>pilot</u> arrived, we knew it would soon be time to take off.
    - ○ **F.** pil • ot
    - ○ **G.** p • il • ot
    - ○ **H.** pilo • t
    - ● **J.** pi • lot

5. At the last minute, Dad jumped out of a <u>taxi</u> and rushed to meet us.
    - ○ **A.** ta • xi
    - ○ **B.** ta • x • i
    - ● **C.** tax • i
    - ○ **D.** t • axi

STOP

Name _____

Spelling Words Beginning with *a* or *be*

Read each sentence. Then find the correct way to spell the missing word. Fill in the circle next to your answer.

1. Dad said I couldn't go to camp with my best friend Lisa _____ I would miss the family trip.

   ● **A.** because   ○ **C.** bacause

   ○ **B.** becaus   ○ **D.** becuz

2. I like family trips, but I don't like it when Lisa is not _____.

   ○ **F.** ahround   ○ **H.** uround

   ○ **G.** arownd   ● **J.** around

3. Dad promised me a surprise _____ we left this summer.

   ○ **A.** befor   ○ **C.** behfore

   ● **B.** before   ○ **D.** bifore

4. As we were about to _____ the trip, Lisa showed up.

   ○ **F.** beggin   ● **H.** begin

   ○ **G.** beegin   ○ **J.** began

5. Dad had made plans for Lisa to go _____ with us for a whole week!

   ○ **A.** aweigh   ○ **C.** awaye

   ○ **B.** ahway   ● **D.** away

Name _____

Vocabulary Dictionary: Antonyms

Read each sentence. Then choose the word that means the opposite of the underlined word. Fill in the circle next to the best answer.

1. Nancy was going to take a <u>difficult</u> test.
   - ○ **A.** hard
   - ○ **B.** long
   - ○ **C.** written
   - ◉ **D.** easy

2. Her sister knew Nancy was too <u>shy</u> to ask for help.
   - ○ **F.** quiet
   - ◉ **G.** bold
   - ○ **H.** nice
   - ○ **J.** timid

3. So her sister offered to <u>give</u> help to Nancy.
   - ◉ **A.** receive
   - ○ **B.** provide
   - ○ **C.** add
   - ○ **D.** supply

4. Every day, her sister helped her study until <u>sunset</u>.
   - ○ **F.** nighttime
   - ◉ **G.** sunrise
   - ○ **H.** evening
   - ○ **J.** morning

5. After all her studying, Nancy felt <u>prepared</u> for the test.
   - ○ **A.** hopeful
   - ○ **B.** ready
   - ◉ **C.** unready
   - ○ **D.** nervous

Name _____

Grammar Comparing with Adjectives

Read each sentence. Find the word that correctly completes the sentence. Fill in the circle next to your answer.

1. Emma is the _____ of the five Miller children.
   - ○ **A.** too young
   - ◉ **C.** youngest
   - ○ **B.** young
   - ○ **D.** younger

2. Yet she is a _____ runner than her sister Sarah.
   - ○ **F.** fastest
   - ○ **H.** most fast
   - ○ **G.** fast
   - ◉ **J.** faster

3. She is also _____ in math than Sarah.
   - ○ **A.** smartest
   - ◉ **C.** smarter
   - ○ **B.** smart
   - ○ **D.** too smart

4. Sarah is the _____ of the Miller children.
   - ○ **F.** quieter
   - ○ **H.** quietly
   - ○ **G.** quiet
   - ◉ **J.** quietest

5. Yet everyone agrees that Sarah is _____ than Emma.
   - ◉ **A.** kinder
   - ○ **C.** kindly
   - ○ **B.** kind
   - ○ **D.** kindest

Smart Solutions

Level 3, Theme 6: Week 3

Weekly Skills Test Record

Student _____ Date _____

Student Record Form

	Possible Score	Criterion Score	Student Score
A: Making Generalizations	5	4	
B: Contractions *'m, 's, 'll, n't, 'd*	5	4	
C: Spelling Contractions	5	4	
D: Vocabulary Dictionary: Spelling Table	5	4	
E: Grammar Adverbs	5	4	
F: Writing Skills Using Exact Adverbs	5	4	
TOTAL	30	24	
Total Student Score x 3.33 =			%

Name _____

Making Generalizations

Read this passage. Then read each question. Fill in the circle next to the best answer.

Too Many Sisters

Terry stomped out of the room she shared with her three younger sisters and yelled, "Who took my purple hair band and my flowered T-shirt? Lisa? Emily? You're always taking my things!"

In the one bathroom the children shared, she found her glitter-pink nail polish spilled on her favorite magazine. The magazine was even ripped and crumpled. As usual, wet towels were in a pile on the floor. "Sarah! Sarah, where are you?" No one answered. "Why can't they leave me alone?" she complained to herself.

Terry stormed back into the bedroom and found one of her two brothers sitting on her bed. "What are you doing, Bryan? Did someone say you could come in here?" He silently shook his head. Terry sighed heavily but didn't say anything else to Bryan. She knew he would miss her.

Terry hurriedly looked around for her sleeping bag but couldn't find it among the clothes, toys, and books that littered the floor. "I need my own room. I can never find anything in here!" Terry thought to herself.

Terry grabbed her things and hurried downstairs with Bryan running behind. When she opened the front door, she stared in amazement. There stood her sisters and brothers holding a banner that said *World's Best Big Sister! We'll miss you. Have fun at camp!* Lisa was wearing the purple hair band. Emily was wearing the flowered T-shirt. Sarah's nails were glittery pink.

They all waved and shouted good-bye as the car pulled away.

Go on

1. What generalization does Terry make about her sisters?
    - ○ **A.** They take her flowered shirts.
    - ◐ **B.** They are always taking her things.
    - ○ **C.** They take her hair bands.
    - ○ **D.** They all share one bathroom.

2. Which detail supports the generalization that Terry's little sisters always make a mess?
    - ○ **F.** Bryan is sitting on Terry's bed.
    - ○ **G.** Terry asks why she can't be left alone.
    - ○ **H.** Sarah doesn't answer when Terry calls for her.
    - ◐ **J.** Wet towels are left on the bathroom floor.

3. Which detail supports the generalization that Terry can never find anything in her room?
    - ○ **A.** Terry sighs when Bryan shakes his head.
    - ○ **B.** Terry complains that she needs her own room.
    - ◐ **C.** Terry can't find her sleeping bag.
    - ○ **D.** All the sisters share one room.

4. Which detail supports the generalization that younger brothers and sisters look up to their older brothers and sisters?
    - ○ **F.** Bryan runs down the stairs behind Terry.
    - ○ **G.** Terry's sisters are wearing her clothes.
    - ◐ **H.** The sign reads *World's Best Big Sister!*
    - ○ **J.** Everyone waved as Terry left.

5. What generalization can you make about Terry's sisters wearing her things at the end of the story?
    - ◐ **A.** It is a way of showing that they will miss her.
    - ○ **B.** Sisters always take things from each other.
    - ○ **C.** They can't wait for her to leave.
    - ○ **D.** They don't have things of their own.

STOP

B

Name _____

Contractions *'m, 's, 'll, n't, 'd*

Read each sentence. Choose the words that stand for the underlined word. Fill in the circle next to the best answer.

1. <u>I'm</u> not very good at soccer, but I love going to the games.
   - ○ **A.** I would
   - ○ **B.** It is
   - ○ **C.** I can
   - ◉ **D.** I am

2. My best friend says <u>he's</u> going to be captain of the team.
   - ○ **F.** he did
   - ◉ **G.** he is
   - ○ **H.** he would
   - ○ **J.** he will

3. My sisters think <u>they'll</u> both make the soccer team.
   - ○ **A.** they would
   - ◉ **B.** they will
   - ○ **C.** they were
   - ○ **D.** there will

4. I <u>don't</u> want to miss out on all the fun.
   - ◉ **F.** do not
   - ○ **G.** did not
   - ○ **H.** will not
   - ○ **J.** does not

5. The coach said <u>he'd</u> let me be the equipment manager!
   - ○ **A.** he did
   - ○ **B.** he is
   - ◉ **C.** he would
   - ○ **D.** he will

STOP

Name _____

Spelling Contractions

Read each sentence. Then find the correct way to spell the missing word. Fill in the circle next to your answer.

1. "Why _____ you looking forward to the family trip?" my mom said.

   ⦿ **A.** aren't   ○ **C.** are'nt
   ○ **B.** arent   ○ **D.** arnt'

2. "I am," I said. "_____ just unhappy about being away from my best friend Max."

   ○ **F.** Im   ⦿ **H.** I'm
   ○ **G.** Im'   ○ **J.** 'Im

3. "Max will be at Camp Arrowhead while _____ be across the ocean."

   ○ **A.** Ill'   ○ **C.** Il'l
   ○ **B.** I'lle   ⦿ **D.** I'll

4. "I know you feel sad because you _____ be with Max," my mom said.

   ○ **F.** wont'   ○ **H.** wo'nt
   ⦿ **G.** won't   ○ **J.** wont

5. "But _____ going to have use of a computer and so are you. So you can e-mail each other."

   ○ **A.** hes   ○ **C.** hes'
   ⦿ **B.** he's   ○ **D.** h'es

D Name _____

Vocabulary Dictionary: Spelling Table

Study the spelling table below. Use the table to find the answer to each question. Fill in the circle next to the best answer.

Sound	Spellings	Sample Words
/ă/	a, au	bat, have, laugh
/ā/	a, ai	made, later, rain
	ay, ea	play, great
/â/	air, ar, are	fair, scarce, care
	eir, ere	their, where
/ä/	a, al	father, calm

1. What vowel sound is in the sample word *laugh?*
   - ● **A.** /ă/
   - ○ **B.** /ā/
   - ○ **C.** /ä/
   - ○ **D.** /â/

2. Which word has the same vowel spelling as the sample word *play?*
   - ● **F.** subway
   - ○ **G.** pattern
   - ○ **H.** shook
   - ○ **J.** under

Go on ⇨

3. Which sample word has the same vowel sound as the word *cable?*

- ○ **A.** rain
- ○ **B.** fair
- ○ **C.** calm
- ○ **D.** laugh

4. What are two spellings of the vowel sound you hear in the sample word *father?*

- ○ **F.** ay, ea
- ○ **G.** air, ar
- ○ **H.** a, al
- ○ **J.** eir, ere

5. What sample words have the vowel sound /â/?

- ○ **A.** father, calm
- ○ **B.** later, play
- ○ **C.** have, laugh
- ○ **D.** care, their

Name _____

Grammar Adverbs

Read each sentence. Find the word that correctly completes the sentence. Fill in the circle next to your answer.

1. At lunchtime, Allen remembered to eat _____, just as his mom had told him.
   - ○ **A.** everywhere
   - ◉ **C.** slowly
   - ○ **B.** sadly
   - ○ **D.** angrily

2. His brother Jack _____ tapped Allen's shoulder.
   - ○ **F.** gentle
   - ○ **H.** gentler
   - ◉ **G.** gently
   - ○ **J.** gentlest

3. Allen turned _____.
   - ○ **A.** today
   - ◉ **C.** around
   - ○ **B.** slow
   - ○ **D.** often

4. "Eat _____, please," said Jack. "We're leaving for the movies in ten minutes."
   - ◉ **F.** faster
   - ○ **H.** never
   - ○ **G.** loudly
   - ○ **J.** secretly

5. Allen laughed. "I guess I'll finish lunch _____," he said.
   - ◉ **A.** later
   - ○ **C.** latest
   - ○ **B.** lately
   - ○ **D.** lateness

STOP

Writing Skills Using Exact Adverbs

Read each sentence. Then choose the sentence that has an adverb which tells how or when. Fill in the circle next to the best answer.

1. ○ **A.** Katy woke up and stretched.
    ◉ **B.** Katy woke up early.
    ○ **C.** Katy couldn't wake up.
    ○ **D.** Katy woke up and smiled.

2. ○ **F.** She thought about her friend's slumber party.
    ○ **G.** She thought about her best friend's party.
    ○ **H.** She thought about her friend's big party.
    ◉ **J.** She thought excitedly about her friend's party.

3. ◉ **A.** Katy quickly planned ways to earn money for a gift.
    ○ **B.** Katy planned ways to earn money for a birthday gift.
    ○ **C.** Katy planned ways to earn money for an expensive gift.
    ○ **D.** Katy planned ways to earn spending money for a gift.

4. ○ **F.** She weeded the garden and washed the car.

○ **G.** She weeded the garden and washed the new car.

◉ **H.** She soon weeded the garden and washed the car.

○ **J.** She weeded the rose garden and washed the car.

5. ○ **A.** When her mother paid her, Katy headed to the music store.

◉ **B.** When her mother paid her, Katy eagerly headed to the store.

○ **C.** When her mother and father paid her, Katy headed to the store.

○ **D.** When her mother paid her, Katy headed to the store on her bike.